9-16-21
I want the abundan[t]
life you offer, Jesus!

EXAMINING MYSELF

EXAMINING MYSELF

*One Woman's Story of Breast
Cancer Treatment and
Recovery*

MUSA MAYER

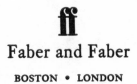

Faber and Faber

BOSTON • LONDON

Library of Congress Cataloging-in-Publication Data

Mayer, Musa.
    Examing myself : one woman's story of breast cancer treatment and recovery / Musa Mayer.
      p. cm.
    ISBN 0-571-19828-7
    1. Mayer, Musa—Health. 2. Breast—Cancer—Patients—Biography. I. Title.
    RC280.B8M35 1993
    362.1'9699449'0092—dc20
    [B]   93-21598
                                              CIP

Jacket design by Don Leeper

Jacket photograph by Michael Eschenbach

Printed in the United States of America

For

Miriam, Eva, Penny, Pat, Helen, Rosa, Anne, Ronnie
and all the others . . .

Together, we discover our strength.

Contents

EXAMINING MYSELF

That Other Place

Illness is the night-side of life, a more onerous citizenship. Everyone who is born holds dual citizenship, in
the kingdom of the well and in the kingdom of the sick.
Although we all prefer to use only the good passport,
sooner or later each of us is obliged, at least for a spell,
to identify ourselves as citizens of that other place.
— SUSAN SONTAG,
Illness as Metaphor

EVERY RESTLESS NIGHT contains a point beyond which the notion of sleep becomes a charade, and ceases to be a real possibility.
Yet how hard to surrender, to admit defeat. Better to lie there
grimly, hour after hour, accruing the insomniac's nightly investment in
futility: the countless shifts of position, the repeated untangling of bed-
clothes and punching of pillows, all the long, intricate trains of thought
leading nowhere.

I sit up and swing my legs over the side of the bed, glancing in the dim
light at my husband's sleeping form, turned away from me. I can see the
regular rise and fall of the covers, hunched around his shoulders. Lately,
I have been feeling flashes of something close to hatred for the ease with
which he drifts off to sleep. Each night when I lie beside him, I listen
for the moment when his breathing deepens and becomes regular. How
I envy him that casual oblivion.

It's as if he were taking a lovely voyage somewhere and leaving me behind. His soft snoring in my ear, which I have never really minded before,
becomes maddening. I prod him in the ribs, and he obligingly turns over
without complaint, only to begin snoring again a moment later.

The green eye of the clock radio blinks. Should I take something? I pick up the plastic vial, shake it and put it down again. There are three pills left, to be saved for real emergencies. Robin's-egg–blue ovals with the seductive name 'Halcion,' they can be depended upon for hours of drugged unconsciousness. Like their namesake, the legendary halcyon bird, they exert a calming, peaceful influence.

Quietly shutting our bedroom door, I step into the hallway of the darkened apartment and begin my nightly prowl. I always go to the window first. I don't know what it is that I hope to see there. Our living room faces north, toward upper Broadway, where the Bromley, a luxury high-rise apartment building, turns its dark and implacable glass facade to me.

But no, there is one light—a fellow sufferer—there, in the 22nd-floor penthouse. I wonder who this person is; what the cause for sleeplessness might be. A sick child, a lost job, a death? Perhaps it is a woman whose reason for insomnia mirrors mine. It could easily be. There are so many of us, more recruits every year to this involuntary sisterhood.

She could be wondering, as I am, when life will resume its sense of normalcy, of safety. At this very moment, she could be turning a bottle of pills over in her hand and rationing them out to invite sleep or stave off panic. Perhaps she is feeling that crushing loneliness that comes from the certain knowledge that the people you love most do not—cannot—understand.

Above the setbacks of the building, the sky is a deep orangy mauve city sky color. But for an occasional cruising cab, and the used magazines the homeless sell still neatly arrayed on the sidewalk, the streets are empty. Looking up Broadway, I watch the lights change in synchrony, staggered two blocks at a time, a flow of green, then red.

There is ritual to this night prowling: the cup of herbal tea, the slice of lightly-buttered toast, the settling down to read or to write in my journal. Avoiding the rebuke of the clock, I try to enjoy the quiet, the time to myself, as if it were a treat, a choice.

It is, in a certain way. Relieved of the need for pretense, I become more myself late at night, more complete and relaxed than I am in the daytime, around other people and the pressures of the healthy world. No need to hide or conceal, or to act as if everything's okay when it's not. It is the comfort of not feeling judged or observed, the comfort of old, stretched-out shoes and loose-fitting garments.

But there is more to this ease, I think. Cherished perceptions of myself

4

as strong and capable have had to be jettisoned these last few years. My illness has forced a regression of sorts. I've had to make friends with a younger, more emotional version of the adult woman I thought I was, a childish self who awakens at odd hours, demanding her due.

Late at night, she is close to me; I can feel the fluttering in my chest, a warmth behind my eyes. I don't want to encounter her, yet she tampers with my sleep, demanding her turn. I don't care much for her, this petulant little girl.

Yet unless I embrace her I find myself floundering helplessly, trying to maintain the illusion of strength and control. Here, in this other place, she has become my guide, my voice, the teller of truths.

Time passes, and the city moves imperceptibly toward morning. A garbage truck outside begins to grind. Waiting for the descent of the heaviness that will let me know it is safe to go back to bed, I drowse and wake, afraid that if I move, sleep will desert me again.

Writing in my journal in these hours before dawn, I am like an emigré to another, darker country, trying to sort out what my new identity means. Night by night, I venture farther into this territory, exploring the contours and features of its strange landscape.

Somewhere out there in that darkness are hundreds of thousands of women like myself, the new citizens of this other country, a huge army of the wounded, each believing herself to be alone in her shock and grief, with no target for her anger, no answering voice for her loss. In one moment of discovery, these lives have been transformed, just as mine has been, as surely as if they had been plucked from their native land and forced to survive in a hostile new landscape, fraught with dangers, real and imagined.

This book is about that landscape, that other place.

It's been a long way back.

Unless we die in a sudden accident, crime, or act of war, most of us will face a serious illness at some point in our lives. We will have to cope somehow with a shorter or longer period of physical diminishment, pain, and uncertainty.

"Considering how common illness is, how tremendous the spiritual change that it brings, how astonishing, when the lights of health go down, the undiscovered countries that are then disclosed," wrote Virginia Woolf, "—when we think of this, as we are so frequently forced to think of it, it becomes strange indeed that illness has not taken its place with love and battle and jealousy among the prime themes of literature."

Not much has changed since 1930, when Woolf published her essay, "On Being Ill." Now, as then, being sick is as common and as diverse an event in human affairs as, say, falling in love, leaving home, or having a child. Certainly, it can be as life-changing. Yet the experience of living with a disease remains to a surprising extent unarticulated, beyond the usual inspirational memoirs, problem-movies-of-the-week, and self-help nostrums for overcoming this or that difficulty in life.

Illness is not a popular destination. No one travels there by choice. While we fear it, we may never have read, or thought, or talked about what it will actually be like for us when we get there. We may know all there is to know about the symptoms of disease, but the actual experience of being ill remains a *terra incognita*, until we are forced to explore it for ourselves.

Dwelling on generalities is no remedy, however. In these pages, I have tried to tell the story of a particular affliction, as it has touched and altered a particular life. It is only that, but it is, I hope, all of that.

Breast cancer has changed my life, in ways I am still discovering, even as I write this. It is more than a disease of the body, far more than the sum of errant cells run wild. Like any life-threatening illness, cancer invades the entire context of a life, disturbing its balance, heightening its struggles. Writing about my illness has provided for me a sort of armature upon which I can deposit, as a sculptor does bits of wet clay, the raw substance of memory and experience to form a new image, a new sense of who I am.

Disease holds all of us hostage to our childhood terrors. A critical illness catapults us back there, to that primitive, emotional state, reminding us that life is circular, that where we are going is where we came from.

6

I was twenty-four years old—not quite an adult, but no longer a child, and with two children of my own—when I had my first brush with the possibility of cancer.

We were living in a rent-controlled tenement apartment on the Lower East Side of Manhattan, barely scraping by on my first husband's salary as a shop teacher at a Long Island private school. I stayed home and took care of the children, having given up a secretarial job when my first child was born.

Some months after my youngest son was born, I found a hardening, or thickening, in my left breast. I didn't call it a lump, at first. That word was too ominous. Jonathan was newly weaned, and so I decided that the mass, whatever it was, must have something to do with the milk glands. Surely, it would go away in time.

But it didn't. Occasionally, I would gingerly touch my breast, or brush against the place where the thickening was with my hand or wrist. I'd experience a rush of anxiety, then hastily put it out of my mind. It was nothing, I reassured myself. I was too busy with the children. We didn't have the money. And as if it were a simple matter, with minor consequences, like going to the dentist, or returning a library book, I continued to procrastinate.

The lump in my breast had been there for eight or nine months before I sought a doctor's advice. The internist referred me to a surgeon, which alarmed me. On my first visit, the surgeon took a long, hollow needle and stuck it into my breast, in an attempt to aspirate what he thought would be a fluid-filled cyst. The syringe remained dry.

His face darkened. "At your age, these lumps are almost certainly benign," he told me. "But I think we'd better make sure."

Back in 1967, breast biopsies were rarely, if ever, done on an outpatient basis, or under local anesthesia. It was still the era of the "one-step" operation. In these procedures, a frozen section of the biopsied tumor would be rushed to pathology to determine if the tissue was malignant while the surgeon waited with the unconscious patient in the operating room. If it was, a mastectomy would be performed. If not, the incision was simply closed. Convenient for surgeons, a "one-step" meant signing a consent form for mastectomy before you even knew you had cancer. It meant going under anesthesia, uncertain of what you'd wake up with, or without.

I shared a hospital room with three other women. Across from my bed an elderly, demented woman who had broken her hip moaned in pain, calling out incoherently every few minutes for the entire three days I was in the hospital. The rest of us kept trying to make her more comfortable, to no avail. One of the other women had already had a mastectomy when I arrived. She kept her curtain drawn, but I could hear her weeping. The woman in the bed next to mine was waiting for a biopsy, as I was.

The preoperative medication, a stinging shot in the hip, must have been some kind of opiate, because I lay there, floating in a woozy state of grace. But I paid dearly for that lovely feeling later, after the surgery. Over-sedated, I fought my way back to consciousness, driven by the urge to know. Nausea broke over me in a sour wave. There was a big bandage on my chest, and pain beneath it. I couldn't tell if I still had my breast or not. Between the retching and my confused state of mind, it seemed like an eternity before I was able to ask. A nurse bent to slip a kidney-shaped pan under my chin. "You're okay, dear," she said. "The tumor was benign."

The room was very quiet when I returned from surgery. The bed next to mine was empty, and the old woman with the broken hip was asleep. After two or three hours, they brought my neighbor back from the recovery room. Early that morning, we had gone down together for our biopsies, and groggily wished each other luck. The nurses drew the curtains around her bed. That day, and the next, the woman in the bed next to me was silent, her face turned away toward the window, speaking only to the nurses who came in every four hours with a shot for the pain. From her silence, and the drawn face of her husband, I understood that her news had not been good. I respected her privacy, sensing that my reprieve would seem like an affront to her.

Secretly, I was relieved that she did not confide in me. I was afraid of her pain. We were no longer fellow travelers, and I couldn't bring myself to consider the strange and awful road she had embarked upon. Besides, her reality was far from mine. At twenty-four, my life was just beginning. This woman was old enough to be my mother. At the time, my sense of camaraderie could not stretch to span the generation between us, or our differing diagnoses.

As I write, I wonder about this woman. Is she still alive, or did her cancer take her? Because I don't remember her name, or what she looked like, or even the tone or inflections of her voice, I find myself entertaining the odd fantasy that she could have been me, at forty-six, at the time of my mastectomy. As if life, like memory, doubled back on itself. As if, through the strange sort of time-travel that writing about the past encourages, my present self, and that former girl that I was—half my lifetime ago now—had fleetingly met.

With the danger past, I lay in the hospital bed, wishing myself far away. I was still nauseated from the anesthesia, but glad nonetheless for the special treatment of convalescence, and the brief respite from twenty-four-hour child care.

In time, both the scar and the memory faded. We moved to New Haven for my husband's graduate studies, then to a small town in Ohio, where he taught in a state university and I found work as a secretary at a local college. By the time I was twenty-nine, our marriage was over, and I was living alone with my two sons, pursuing a new career as a mental health counselor.

My second encounter with the threat of breast cancer came when I was in my mid-thirties. By then, I had gotten a graduate degree and was working as a therapist at a drug treatment agency. I was newly remarried. My sons seemed happily occupied with school and friends, soccer and baseball. My life was full and satisfying.

It was my husband Tom who found the lump, this time in my right breast, when we were making love. This time, I didn't wait. I went straight to a surgeon. When he recommended a biopsy, I remembered the nausea and emotional trauma of the last surgery, and I asked if it could be done on an outpatient basis, under a local anesthetic. He agreed, and said that he would make a semi-circular incision, partway around the areola, that would leave an invisible scar.

The procedure was brief; the news, again, was good.

I went home from day surgery in high spirits, even stopping for lunch at a local restaurant, relieved that this biopsy had in no way echoed the ordeal of a dozen years before, and that I would not even have a visible scar, as I did on my other breast. It would be as if the whole thing never even happened.

As the day progressed, however, the area around the incision began to feel swollen and tender. It was just the anesthetic wearing off, I told

9

myself. Finally, toward evening, when my right breast had blown up to almost twice its normal size, I had to admit that something was seriously wrong. It looked like a big, discolored balloon. The skin was tight and hot to the touch. Suddenly, in a gush, an alarming amount of blood began to leak from the incision. Tom called an ambulance.

In the hospital emergency room, my surgeon was gruff, almost angry, as if I had inconvenienced him in some way. He muttered something about local anesthesia sometimes causing this kind of problem, making me feel as if I were responsible for this mess.

I lay there and wept as he worked over me. I was frightened by the amount of blood I seemed to be losing; I could feel it running down my side, soaking the linens beneath me, hot and wet. It took a long time to stop the hemorrhaging. Because the anesthetic kept bleeding out of the tissue, the surgeon had to inject me with the Lidocaine again and again. Even so, I felt each suture.

No one paid any attention to my distress. They were all leaning over my draped chest, as if I weren't even there. At last a nurse, seeing I was crying, took my hand. "Can't they give me something?" I asked her. The nurse whispered to the surgeon, who stopped what he was doing, looked at me without speaking, then gave the order for an injection of Valium.

At last, it was over. They brought Tom in, white-faced. He helped me down from the gurney, and I stood there in my bandages, swaying weakly, registering the bloody footprints and heavily-stained linen wadded on the floor.

I went home outraged and shaken. More than the bleeding episode itself, it was the surgeon's unfeeling treatment of me, his failure to offer a kind or consoling word as he worked to stop the hemorrhaging, that upset me most. Perhaps it was just his own distress that had shown itself as coldness, but I couldn't forgive him.

As for the bleeding, these things did happen, and with some frequency, I discovered later. Something about the local anesthetic collapsing small blood vessels, which later opened and bled. It was possible, too, that the surgeon had been too ambitious, cut through too much tissue in order to make a cosmetic incision.

Ten days later, after he had removed the stitches, I confronted the surgeon about his coldness. He leapt up from his chair and opened the door of the examining room. For a moment, I thought he was going to run away without another word. Although he did say something at least mildly placating, I no longer remember what it was. I never saw him again.

Eventually, the bruises faded; purple shaded into yellow, then disappeared. I healed. The external scar was, as promised, invisible. Inside my breast, a knot of scar tissue formed, a hard mass that caused a moment of concern for every doctor who examined me subsequently.

There was another scar within, too, a bitter emotional wound that refused to disappear. Never again, I vowed. Next time, if there was a next time, I would muster the courage to say no to a biopsy. I would trust my own intuition. Such outrage I felt at the time—such purposeful and sure denial—as if by a simple act of will, I had the power to hold back the ongoing rush of events.

But I never really considered the possibility that I might actually have breast cancer. I couldn't think past the immediate experience of the biopsy itself. That seemed more than enough to contend with, at the time.

A decade passed. In 1982, two years after the death of my father, the artist Philip Guston, we decided to move back to New York, where Tom could complete a post-doctoral internship in rehabilitation psychology at Rusk Institute, and I could help my mother deal with my father's estate. For the next several years, the management of his paintings and drawings was to occupy a good deal of my time.

My sons were becoming young men. David went off to college at Sarah Lawrence. Jonathan finished high school at a small private school in New York, and left for his freshman year at Skidmore College.

After ten years of working as a counselor in the Ohio community mental health system, and nearly twice that as a mother, I had grown tired of taking care of people. I wanted to focus on my own life, not that of others. With this in mind, I began to pursue a longtime dream of becoming a writer, taking classes and workshops to learn the craft of fiction. Meanwhile, Tom's work as a neuropsychologist had led him into the field of cognitive rehabilitation, a treatment for head injury, and he had developed a successful program at a rehabilitation center in Manhattan.

The year Jonathan left for college and I turned forty, a routine gynecological exam led to a diagnosis of rapidly growing uterine fibroids, a brief scare about ovarian cancer, and a partial hysterectomy. This dashed any hopes for us having a child of our own—a decision we'd delayed repeatedly, believing there was always time.

I took refuge in my work. After publishing a few short stories, I began graduate studies at Columbia, pursuing a second master's degree, this time in writing. I was working on my thesis novel when, at the age of forty-five, I found another lump, again in my right breast.

Remembering my earlier resolve, I consulted my intuition, which was as little use this time as it had been before. Some of the time, I was sure I was fine; at other moments, I would touch the lump worriedly, and yearn for certainty.

For weeks I walked around in an odd nether state, my fears a constant background noise, contaminating my daily life. Able to forget about it during the day, I would lie in bed at night, unable to sleep. I kept running my fingers over the hard knot of scar tissue to the irregularly-shaped mass beside it, trying to see if the new lump had changed.

It was my insomnia, finally, that drove me to make an appointment with my gynecologist, after more than a month of this nightly ritual. To my enormous relief, he read the radiologist's report on my mammogram, examined my breasts, and told me I had nothing to worry about. It was only a cyst.

I didn't think to question how he knew this. I had heard what I wanted to hear. The insomnia disappeared. Once a month, in a desultory way, I would examine my breasts, always finding the lump still there, but reminding myself that the doctor had told me it was no cause for concern.

With the clarity that hindsight affords, this whole chain of events leading up to my eventual diagnosis with breast cancer has come in my mind to assume a sort of tragic inevitability. I can see clearly how one set of fears led to the next poor judgment, which in turn led to the next wrong choice. While I understand my own motivations, it is hard to let go of the self-recrimination, the "if onlys."

How could I not have realized what was happening to me? How could I have remained so trusting, as doctor after doctor let me down? The stories above could easily comprise a cautionary tale on how *not* to go about dealing with a suspected cancer.

Yet I had my own defensible reasons, at the time, all along the way. There was so much I didn't know. So much I didn't know I needed to know.

For almost a year, I did nothing. Caught up as I was in graduate school, and with the publication of my first book, I barely thought about the lump. When I did, I reassured myself with the gynecologist's pronouncement. Only a cyst.

Then, on my next routine visit, the gynecologist expressed alarm that the mass was still there, and he did what he should have done the year before: he referred me to a breast surgeon.

It was not a discrete lump, he confirmed, but an irregular shaped thickening and therefore difficult to assess. After six weeks of further observation, he recommended an excisional (surgical) biopsy, to remove the mass so that a pathologist could examine it. A needle biopsy—which drew out, through a fine needle, a few cells from several different sites in the lump—had proved negative. I was told that this was an inconclusive test, but with unfailing optimism or naiveté, I took it to mean that I was all right.

I was mistaken. Because it doesn't sample all the tumor tissue, a needle biopsy is not considered conclusive unless it is positive. If malignant cells *are* found through needle biopsy, however, the diagnosis of cancer is certain. The surgeon and patient can then bypass the lesser procedure of excisional biopsy and proceed directly to immediate lumpectomy, which removes more tissue than biopsy, or to mastectomy, which removes the entire breast.

Even then, my concern was solely with the biopsy procedure itself. I told the surgeon about my two previous experiences, the bleeding, the severe nausea from the anesthetic, exacting his reassurance that this time, it would be different.

And it was, although not in the way I anticipated.

TWO

Hour of Lead

This is the Hour of Lead—
Remembered, if outlived,
As Freezing persons, recollect the Snow—
First—Chill—then Stupor—then the letting go—
— Emily Dickinson

A N INCH FROM my eyes, the expanse of fabric crosses my vision
as far as I can see, an entire landscape of small, fuzzy green dots
against a white ground. Like a baby's cotton flannel receiving
blanket, I think, momentarily comforted by the image. Above me somewhere, the great eye of the light is shining. A radio plays classical music.

I am cold, lying naked under the thin cotton sheets and blanket with
my bare buttocks against the greased metal grounding plate. Behind this
flimsy cloth barrier that separates my head from the rest of me, I am
more aware of what is going on than I would like to be. I cannot see
the neatly-draped window that exposes my breast, the cold, brown an-
tiseptic that trickles down my side, the surgeon's gloved hands, his eyes.
I don't feel the incision itself, but only the tugs and pinches that are the
mute objections of numbed flesh.

I can't quite figure out what to do with the fact that I am lying here,
awake, undrugged. I feel like an uninvited guest, as if I am eavesdrop-
ping. Shall I try to decipher the cursory conversation, or think of other
things?

Then the music stops and there is silence, broken only by the clink
of metal against metal, the surgeon's instruction to label the tissue
samples.

The smell of burnt flesh from the electrocautery means the biopsy is almost finished. Willing my muscles to relax, I close my eyes and let my mind wander. I am reviewing our plans for a trip to Spain and southern France in two weeks when I feel the surgeon's hand on my arm. "I'll see you in an hour," he says. "Upstairs in my office."

Before I can say anything, he is gone.

In the recovery room, they sit me in a reclining chair and wrap me in warm blankets. They bring me apple juice and tea, and, after a few minutes, my husband.

"How are you?" he asks. "How did it go?"

"It was nothing," I tell him. Not entirely true, but close enough. Luxuriating in the comfortable chair, I feel pampered, and a bit guilty for lapping up all this solicitous attention when there's nothing really wrong with me.

We smile at one another. All I can think of is, it's over.

I am still feeling nothing but relief an hour later, as I sit in the surgeon's waiting room. Although the incision is beginning to throb, I feel lighter than air, free of the anxiety of recent weeks. It's a warm spring day, and I want to be outside, enjoying it, away from this place.

"Mrs. Mayer." The nurse is beckoning me. Tom stands up, too, but only I am admitted.

"In a minute," she says to him. "The doctor wants to examine her first."

I have not yet perched myself on the examining table when the surgeon comes in. He closes the door and turns to me, ignoring my unbuttoned blouse.

His face is grim. "I'm afraid it was malignant," he says. His head swims toward me in the liquid air, like a large, strange growth of some kind. I grab the edge of the examining table.

I am shaking all over and my face feels as if it will ignite with sudden heat. I can't absorb this.

He takes my icy hands in his and makes me look at him. "Listen, you're going to be all right," he says. "You're going to be fine."

He leads me to the chair. "Sit down for a minute."

"I want my husband."

"I'll get him. You stay here."

Alone in the little room, I feel my face stretching into a grimace of grief. My sobbing is like a dry, involuntary retching. There are no tears.

Controlling myself, I get up and pace the room, muttering, shaking my head. This can't be happening. Not to me. Not to us.

The doctor leads me into his office, where Tom is sitting. I can see from his face that he's already been told, and I feel an absurd gratitude that at least I am spared the second shock of seeing that first dreadful moment register on him.

It was later, much later, that it occurred to me that this breast surgeon must have had to orchestrate many such moments, perhaps even daily, and had obviously given some thought to how best to do it. The man's tact was impeccable.

After a minute or two, he left us alone in his office, closing the door so that we could have some privacy. After seeing his last two patients of the afternoon, he would return, he promised, to give us all the time we needed.

By the time he came back to answer our questions, the first wave of shock and tears had crested over us and passed, leaving us drained and terrified.

All I knew about breast cancer was that some women had mastectomies and others had lumpectomies, and that chemotherapy made you deathly ill. My sister-in-law Sandy had died from breast cancer, but I had heard of at least one woman, a friend of my mother's, who'd had a mastectomy a dozen years ago and was still alive.

Despite the fact that this was my third biopsy and that I'd been having regular mammograms for years, I had never, even for a moment, believed I could actually get breast cancer. I still held stock in the illusion of a just universe.

I had some choices to make in the next week or two, the surgeon was saying. I should seek other opinions; his receptionist would help me to set up the appointments. He would go ahead and schedule me for surgery in ten days, just to have the space reserved. If I elected to have a mastectomy, I could have immediate reconstruction, if I wanted. He'd give me the name of a plastic surgeon he worked with. If I chose a lumpectomy, I'd have to have five weeks of radiation treatments. The head of radiation oncology at the hospital could evaluate whether or not I was a good candidate for breast-conserving surgery. All other things being equal, he told me, the survival rates would be the same, with either operation. Both operations would also involve an axillary dissection, where the lymph nodes under my arm would be removed and examined for the spread of cancer.

As far as the tumor itself went, they would know more from the pathology report, which would take a few days. From gross examination, he could tell us that it had poorly-defined margins and was on the large side. These were not positive signs. Still, the chances were good that it had not spread to the lymph nodes.

"How large?" Tom asked.

"It's hard to say."

"Yes, but if you were to estimate."

"It was irregular in shape," he said. "How large is your mustache?"

Tom leaned forward. I could see his face getting red. "Excuse me?"

"About three centimeters," the doctor said. "I would guess it was about three centimeters."

We were silent a moment, still trying to stretch our minds around the enormity of what had happened.

"You told me I'm going to be all right," I said. "How can you know that?"

"With the best treatment, your chances are excellent."

"What does that mean?"

"I don't like to give my patients percentages, or odds. They're meaningless for the individual. But your chances are excellent."

"Will I have to have chemotherapy?" I asked, suddenly realizing that chemo—not losing my breast, or even my life—was my worst fear.

"Let's just get you past this first hurdle," he told me. "Then we can talk about it."

After giving us his weekend phone number and making an appointment to see us the following Tuesday, he ushered us to the door.

The waiting room was empty. I thought of the times I'd sat there, idly examining the faces of women emerging from the surgeon's office, reading them for clues. Had there been anyone there that day to see our reddened eyes and grim expressions, they could scarcely have failed to know what had happened.

The receptionist, ordinarily a dour, short-tempered woman, adopted a newly compassionate manner and spent half an hour setting up consultations, tests, and the surgery itself. Alarmed by this special treatment, I stood at the window, my appointment book spread open before me.

Waiting for her to complete her phone calls, I leafed through the itinerary of our trip to Europe that I had penciled into my Filofax. Madrid, Barcelona, Arles, Nice. Damn it all, I thought, I spent a lot of time planning this trip! All those charming small hotels I'd written to, the money orders in francs I'd had to buy. All of that effort, wasted. For one mad moment I entertained the idea that we could do it anyway. Act as if nothing had happened.

Tom and I emerged from the hospital into the late afternoon sunlight and got into a taxi. Although the anesthetic was wearing off, I barely felt the pain from the biopsy incision. What I did feel was numb. It was as if I were carrying a bowl of icy liquid, filled to the brim, that threatened to slop over at every moment. Every bump, every car horn and loud voice, was an assault. I just wanted to get home.

It was Friday afternoon, and my next appointment was not until Monday. The idea of waiting out the weekend without knowing more made me desperate. Through Tom's brother Donald, a surgeon, we were able to find out the name of a recent textbook on breast cancer, one that my surgeon, I learned later, used in his teaching. A friend rushed to a medical bookstore before closing and brought it to us.

That night, I gave myself a crash course on my disease. I sat up until dawn the next morning reading an 800-page tome entitled *Cancer of the Breast*. I steeled myself to look at the diagrams of surgery, and tried to make sense of chapters on pathology, cell kinetics, staging, primary treatment, adjuvant therapy and reconstruction.

My longterm interest in medicine—along with the medical dictionary beside me—made it possible for me to follow most of what I was reading; there were even a few moments, during those long hours, when the exhilaration of learning almost displaced the fear. But then a chapter summary would catch me up short. At the end of the section on staging and primary treatment, I found this chilling statement: "Thus, the extent of disease must be considered the major, perhaps the ultimate, determinant of prognosis."

Hardest to read were not the passages on surgery, with their alarming illustrations, but the charts and graphs of statistics on recurrence and prognosis. Factors like tumor size, location and histopathology, type of surgery, differing protocols of chemotherapeutic agents, and axillary lymph node involvement all appeared to be crucial; survival was expressed in five- and ten-year increments, and was "relative" or "disease-free." Each factor had its own little graph of descending lines and percentages, where survival was mapped over time. I read and reread these ominous little charts, with no idea of how to combine them in any way that would reflect my particular circumstances, most of which were not yet known.

At the end of a chapter on chemotherapy, I found this little gem: "It has not been resolved, if adjuvant therapy merely delays relapse or truly improves overall survival."

Charts, graphs and columns of percentiles aside, this textbook, for all its technical language, also made me realize that oncology, the medical speciality that deals with cancer and its treatment, was far from being an exact science. Sudden breakthroughs are rare in cancer research. Any precision in treatment is the result of painstaking studies where thousands of patients have been willing to submit to experimental treatment protocols.

Often the results of such studies aren't fully clear for decades. This is particularly true with breast cancer, which is usually slow-growing as cancers go. At the time of my own diagnosis, for example, three major studies of adjuvant treatment (chemotherapy and hormonal therapy that immediately follows surgery) for breast cancer had just published preliminary data that showed a small but significant disease-free survival with the treatment. However, the data covered only three to four years; an actual cure could not yet be demonstrated, only a difference in time to recurrence.

The confusion I felt wasn't only from the shock of diagnosis or the welter of new information. This was only the tip of a great, bleak iceberg of unknowns. The more I found out, the clearer it became how little was known about this cluster of diseases known as breast cancer. Once you had it, you could be cured, or the cancer could return to kill you in two years, or ten, or thirty, and no one knew why, any more than they knew what had caused it in the first place. I would have to live with partial knowledge, partial certainty, crude treatments, painful side effects, with no sure expectation of anything.

Somewhere toward morning, I realized that it was not five- and ten-year survival that should concern me now, but just getting through the next week or two, a day at a time.

When I sank into a bleary stupor beside my husband, it was almost dawn. I was able to sleep. At least, the vast, feared unknown had been replaced by a specific body of knowledge, however confusing and alarming.

All that week, I wore that knowledge like a shield. Over the next days, I found other articles from medical journals, and books written for the lay person that clarified the issues further. I raided bookstores, discovered medical libraries open to the public. I called a cancer information hotline and was relieved to find out that what they said confirmed my understanding.

We began to tell our friends and family. "I'm afraid I've had some rather bad news," I would say, reminded of how it had felt to break the news of my father's death to his friends. It was hard to hear those first reactions of shock and dismay. Their upset made me retreat further into the cocoon of dispassionate information I'd been weaving around myself.

I kept remembering how I'd felt in the past, hearing this kind of diagnosis, how my first thought had always been of people I'd known who had died from the disease. That was the equation: cancer equals death. I wasn't alone in this perception. As far as the world was concerned, I had started down a road whose destination was bleak. Even though we've all been told a hundred times by the American Cancer Society that death is not the inevitable consequence of the disease, there is still that first reaction. Only AIDS has the power to provoke more dread.

As I shared what I knew, I could sense the unspoken weight of other questions that went unasked, the same questions that consumed me, too, and that all boiled down to one: would I survive? Already, I had read enough to know that I couldn't expect an answer to this, that the best I could hope for was the dubious hedge of majority percentages: seventy to eighty percent of all women with breast cancer are still alive after five years. That didn't mean that they wouldn't die from the disease in the sixth or tenth or fifteenth year. On the other hand, they could very well live out a normal life-span. Because breast cancer is slow-growing, the usual five-year survival landmark has less meaning. Unlike some other cancers, it can recur at any time.

I tried to fill in as many facts as I could from my new and patchy fund of partial knowledge. In talking about the disease, I found myself viewing the whole process objectively, as if it were happening to someone else. I referred to "the breast," or "the cancer," as if it were a subject for curiosity. I caught myself reassuring others, adopting an efficient, matter-of-fact tone.

There were a few people we didn't tell right away. I was concerned about my mother, who was very frail, and decided I would tell her in person the following weekend, before I went in for surgery.

In between the telephone calls, I felt stunned and helpless. Lack of sleep heightened my feelings of unreality. Periodically, as the weekend wore on, Tom and I would meet in the kitchen, embrace, and burst into tears. In between bouts of crying, reading, and our intense talks and phone calls, we took walks, and even went out to a movie. It seemed important to both of us that our lives maintain some semblance of normalcy.

Aside from Tom's brother Donald, who had been through this with his first wife, and who, as a physician, could answer many of our medical questions, we didn't want to see anyone. Being together had taken on a new intensity. Tom and I felt isolated with our pain, and protective of that isolation.

The next night I fell asleep easily enough, for I had been exhausted. But I woke up after only two hours, heart pounding, mind racing. Not wanting to disturb Tom, I sat up again in the darkened living room and read.

All that night long I read and reread the material I'd collected on breast cancer, looking for something that wasn't there. I felt as if I were putting together a giant jigsaw puzzle for which I had only a few pieces, without even the benefit of the final picture as a guide.

Yet I knew I had to do something, anything, to stem the flow of uncertainties that kept coming at me. I kept searching for information. What I failed to realize at the time was that the physical facts of disease can never fully address its impact, the totality of what it is like to live with cancer. Knowledge alone couldn't control what was happening to me, but I clung to the notion that informing myself could keep me from being pulled under by its strong current.

I needed something more than reading could provide. What I needed, I decided, was to meet and talk with others who had faced what I was facing, to know first-hand what having breast cancer had been like for them—not the details of their diagnosis and treatment so much as the actual experience of illness.

During that interminable ten days between diagnosis and surgery, in between the examinations and tests and consultations, I found time to talk at length with several women who had undergone surgery and chemotherapy for breast cancer within the previous year.

Without exception, I found that they were eager to talk to me. Often, I had the sense that they were grateful for the opportunity to put their feelings about the illness into words. They spoke openly of their distress and apprehension, of the difficulties of the surgery and recuperative period, of their fears of chemotherapy and the reality of their treatments, as well as of the satisfactions and setbacks of reconstructive surgery. Some of what they had to say was reassuring—for example, that the post-surgical pain of mastectomy was not severe, and that the chemotherapy treatments had not been, for these women at least, as debilitating as they had feared. Some of what they said was sobering, though. They spoke of the difficulties of living with uncertainty, of how anxiety-ridden their quarterly exams were, of a continuing sense of isolation from family and friends.

"Do you know," one woman mused, "I've told you more in the past hour and a half about what happened to me than I've ever told anyone— even my closest friends."

I knew that I couldn't possibly extrapolate much from a small sample of half a dozen women. What they offered me, most of all, was a sense of what it was like to go through the process, and to survive it, with dignity and reason. They gave me the gift of knowing it was possible.

My experience of illness would be as different, in small and large ways, as each of them was from the other. I realized that. Their diagnoses and prognoses, as well as their treatments and reactions to treatment, had been surprisingly varied. These six women had been treated at four of the five major cancer centers in the New York metropolitan area, obviously by physicians with differing approaches. Each of them had sought second and third—and sometimes fourth and fifth—opinions elsewhere.

"Let them tell you what they think, but then you go and decide for yourself," one woman told me. "You're the one who's going to have to live with what you decide, not them."

"I know it's hard to hear conflicting opinions when you feel so desperate for certainty," said another. "But you'll be glad later that you did. You'll feel like you made your decision for rational reasons, not just out of fear."

"Just remember," a third woman said, "opinions are only opinions. What it means is, they don't really know for sure. It means *you* can decide."

This should have been empowering, but it didn't feel that way at first. Like any woman in my position, I wanted to know that there was one right thing to do. The notion of options was frightening.

Looking back, I can see that these conversations laid the groundwork for something I was to hear again months later from the social worker who led my support group. I didn't like hearing it then, either. Halfway through my chemotherapy, I was floundering around, investigating alternative treatments such as special diets, visualization, homeopathy, and so forth. There had to be some way of knowing the "right" thing to do, I kept insisting.

"Maybe," she said, "you just have to choose what feels right to you."

But I didn't want to hear that. I still wanted to believe in answers and absolutes.

During that long week before the surgery, I had my first taste of being a cancer patient. Every day there were doctors' appointments to keep, tests to take, people to talk to, new materials to read, other resources to investigate. It was a full-time job.

I had entered another world, a world in which the ordinary events of my life had abruptly become irrelevant. None of the ingredients of my former identity counted here. I was meeting the people with whom I would form a peculiarly intimate connection over the next weeks and months—peculiar because our relationships would be one-sided, focusing only on my treatment; and intimate, to me at least, because the outcome of that treatment mattered so very much. I wanted these doctors and nurses and technicians to know who they were dealing with, but that was really impossible. In this stripped-down, streamlined hospital world, they just didn't have time for that sort of thing. I was simply another cancer patient.

Everywhere I went, every laboratory and doctor's office, was packed with people who were obviously ill and in distress. They all had cancer, too. Along with the inevitable sense of depression and apprehension that attends such places, obvious feelings of haste and pressure, and impatience with having to wait too long, filled these waiting rooms to capacity.

Perhaps because I was forearmed with the facts about my disease, it turned out to be the small things that got to me as that interminable week wore on. Receptionists who forgot you were there. A technician in nuclear medicine who never even bothered to say hello, who just taped my shoes together, pulled a huge machine over me until it rested half an inch above my face, and left me there without explanation, while he joked with a co-worker in another room.

There was no physical pain involved with the bone scan; only a shot of radioactive dye two hours before, and the nuisance of having to drink quarts of liquid. I remember lying there on that thin strip of metal, barely padded with a folded sheet, with no place to rest my arms, while the technician laboriously moved the huge blunt block of the machine up and down my body. "Don't move," he'd say, and then he'd disappear for another ten minutes.

From where I lay, I could see my bones taking shape on the computer screen, and my full bladder, like a ghostly balloon of green luminescent dots.

Apart from my irritation with the technician, I was more fascinated than alarmed by this test. I knew that it was routine for breast cancer patients at first diagnosis to have a scan, to rule out metastases to the bone, and to provide a baseline for further testing. As I watched the image develop and saw the architecture of my skeleton emerge in clear detail, I was struck with how anonymous it seemed to be, how much like any other skeleton.

Something in this image was dissonant with my own sense of self. Here I was, looking at the most central part of me, the actual armature of my being. The universality of this Halloween picture was inescapable, even reassuring: I had a skeleton like everyone else, and the leg bone actually *was* connected to the hip bone. Yet, what I saw on the scan seemed irreconcilable with the me that I knew.

As I was lying there, trying not to move as the machine registered its images, it occurred to me that the individuality we pride ourselves upon, our personhood, rests almost entirely on intangible qualities of character and efforts of the mind, all of which are completely invisible to medical technology. Medicine depends on our physical similarities, from which it draws its conclusions. That old truism from the anatomy lab still obtains: We are all the same under the skin. That day, I had visible proof.

For every irritable receptionist and full waiting room that week, there was some balancing act of kindness or consideration. In the quiet luxury of his uptown Park Avenue office, blessedly distant from the hospital, the man who was to become my plastic surgeon spent an unhurried hour explaining reconstructive surgery. He was a tall, handsome man, with dark curly hair and a gentle manner. Like an artist, he had slides of his work to show us. Tom and I passed the viewer back and forth, taking turns looking at reconstructions he had performed. On many of the slides, except for a thin, almost invisible scar, the breast looked perfect, and almost exactly matched its partner.

"These are the best results, right?" I asked.

He nodded.

"What about the ones you're not so happy with? Can we look at some of them?"

"Sure." He handed me another group of slides. Looking at these, I could certainly see why. There was more asymmetry. The reconstructed breast was a little high, or a little less pronounced in shape, or didn't have quite the same droop as the natural breast.

I thought of the pictures I'd seen of mastectomy scars. I thought of having to wear a prosthesis. "I think I could live with this," I told Tom, handing him the slides.

He looked, then returned my smile. "So could I," he said.

After my breast surgeon had removed all the tissue and done the axillary dissection, the plastic surgeon would take over and finish the operation. He would place a tissue expander, a flat but inflatable plastic balloon, where my breast had been. Under my skin, there would be a small "port," connected by tubing to the tissue expander, a nub of plastic through which saline solution could be injected over a period of months, to stretch the skin and promote the growth of new skin. Eventually, a permanent, natural-feeling silicone gel and saline implant would be inserted in the breast-shaped pocket of skin created by the tissue expander. A nipple on the new breast could be created by skin-grafting, and the other breast could be lifted, for improved symmetry.

Two days before, the chief of radiation oncology at the hospital had told me that in his opinion, I was not an ideal candidate for breast-conserving treatment—lumpectomy with radiation. Follow-up to detect a local recurrence of cancer, which happens ten to fifteen percent of the time, would be problematic in my case, he said. Mammography would probably continue to be uninformative, owing to the density of my breast tissue, and even with manual examination it would be difficult to detect anything, with all the scar tissue from the previous, botched biopsy and the frequent lumps and bumps of my cystic condition.

"I'm not saying don't keep your breast," he told me, "Chances are, it would be fine, and you may decide it's important enough to you to put up with the anxiety."

But it wasn't. I knew right away what my decision would be; I had known fifteen minutes after my diagnosis, although it had been only the fear talking then. My breast surgeon had been careful not to intrude with his own opinion, preferring to let me go through the process of consulting others first.

Now, hearing—and seeing—what was possible in terms of immediate reconstructive surgery, I knew I wanted a mastectomy, with immediate reconstruction. For the first time that week, I felt a sense of relief.

In hindsight, I can see how the medical opinions I gathered subtly and not so subtly influenced my decision. Had my breast surgeon encouraged me to have a lumpectomy with radiation, as many surgeons now do, or had I found second and third opinions that supported this option, I might have decided to brave my anxiety and keep my breast.

Having a small tumor confined to a single area and readily accessible to surgery makes breast-conserving surgery a likely option, although these are not the only criteria. Up to fifty percent of women diagnosed with breast cancer are candidates for lumpectomy, though only about half of them choose it. Clearly, the medical community has not been completely won over to the benefits of breast-conserving surgery, despite the fact that large longterm studies comparing lumpectomy plus radiation with mastectomy have shown no difference in overall survival rates, and relatively low rates of local recurrence.

The next day, my tenuous emotional equilibrium was upset all over again when the surgeon I consulted at another major teaching hospital, recommended as the dean of the department of breast surgery there, offered a conflicting opinion. A dignified, white-haired gentleman, this surgeon no longer performed operations himself but only consulted on breast cancer cases.

I watched and waited as he reviewed the pathology report and looked at my slides under his microscope. He put up the two sets of mammograms on the light-box, then took them down. Motioning me to sit on the table, he began to examine me, asking me what had been recommended and if I had come to any conclusions yet.

"Well, the mastectomy is certainly the right decision," he said, after I had answered his questions. "But I'm concerned about one thing. What's the big hurry about this reconstruction business?"

"What do you mean?"

"Just that it's a question of priorities, as I see it. First things first. Saving your life is what's important right now. You can always have reconstruction done later, if you decide you really want to."

But that would mean another surgery, I objected.

"That may be, but by having it done now, you're risking infection, perhaps even the delay of your chemotherapy, and that could have serious consequences."

The doctor poked his cold fingers up under my arm, a frown on his face. "I think I can feel an enlarged lymph node here. Of course it could be just from the biopsy, but . . . " He let the sentence trail off into meaningful silence as I sat there, stunned. I should have been asking a whole list of questions I'd prepared, but I couldn't think straight. I had told Tom I could handle this appointment alone, that he didn't need to come with me. Now I regretted it.

The doctor looked at me. "You can get dressed now."

I buttoned up my blouse, blinking back tears. In less than five minutes, this kindly-looking elderly gentlemen had pitched three curves at me I wasn't prepared for: the swollen, perhaps cancerous, lymph node; the danger of infection posed by immediate reconstruction; and what sounded like a taken-for-granted certainty—in his mind at least—that I would require chemotherapy.

Seeming to take no notice of my upset, he walked back to his desk, sat down and began rereading my file.

I was stunned by the bluntness of his approach. Maybe he thought I was vain, or obsessed with my appearance, and needed to be shocked into reality. Or maybe it was just that thirty or forty years of dealing with cancer patients had hardened him to displays of emotion.

Then I realized that he was waiting for me to pull myself together. My tears gave way to anger. I didn't give a damn how eminent a physician this guy was. In another minute I would grab my slides and reports and march right out of there without another word. I finished dressing and perched on the edge of the chair facing his desk, ready for flight.

"You know," he said after a minute or two of strained silence had passed between us, "I've always thought that these reports of women doing better psychologically after reconstruction are greatly exaggerated. I've never understood why it's necessary, myself. There is some feeling of loss, of course. But it's been my experience that after an adjustment period, most women do just fine after mastectomy."

I wondered how he knew that, if this was all the attention he paid to his patients' emotions. I muttered something unintelligible. I just wanted to get out of there.

Finally, he looked up at me. "You did ask for my opinion," he said. "That *is* why you're here, is it not?"

That was true, perfectly true. It was only that I was unprepared for my own reaction to conflicting messages. I had thought I wanted an opinion; but I suppose what I was really looking for, in my emotional state, was reassurance. I only wanted confirmation of what I had already heard, to know from some other authority that what the doctors I'd already seen had recommended was the right thing to do. Well, the experts were not about to agree. I wasn't going to get that confirmation. Not then, not ever.

The women I'd spoken to were right. However frightening it was to admit, this business of choices in cancer treatment was, past a certain point, largely a matter of intuition, trust, and self-knowledge.

As soon as I got home, I called the plastic surgeon and told him what had happened. The teaching hospital I'd gone to for a second opinion rarely, if ever, did immediate reconstruction, he said. They were known for that, as they were known for recommending unusually aggressive chemotherapy.

About the operation itself, what the plastic surgeon had to say was reassuring. Of the more than one hundred surgeries of this kind that he, personally, had performed, only a handful had involved infection not easily controlled by the routine administration of antibiotics. In only one of these cases did the tissue expander have to be removed, and the woman was able to begin her chemotherapy on schedule.

"A lot of older physicians aren't even aware of the newer techniques we're using now," he told me. "Obviously, they still have biases against reconstruction. I'm sorry you had to hear all that."

"So am I," I said.

Once again, I regained my composure. I realized later that I'd only been offered the option of immediate reconstruction by chance. Probably because of the inconvenience in scheduling two surgeons to perform two sequential surgical procedures—the mastectomy and the implantation of the tissue expander—this is still not a frequently performed operation. Certainly, the majority of women I know who have had breast cancer were not made aware of this possibility at the time of their diagnosis.

Knowing my own attitudes toward surgery, I think that I would have balked at having reconstructive surgery later. Why open up old wounds, quite literally? For all I know, the surgeon to whom I went for that second opinion was right, and I would have made a satisfactory adjustment without it, and be happily—or at least resignedly—wearing a prosthesis today.

Until recently, conventional wisdom in the field maintained that for a satisfactory psychological adjustment, a woman with breast cancer must mourn the loss of her breast before having reconstructive surgery. The process was thought to be analogous to dealing with other losses: no one would deny, for example, that a widow should mourn her husband's death before remarrying.

From my own experience, however, there is no question that the emotional pain of the loss of a breast is eased by the concurrent process of reconstruction. I lived with this feeling every day, as I saw that reassuring curve take form.

At least something positive was happening, I told myself, on the bad days during my chemotherapy. I took a great and probably irrational comfort from the hard balloon of saline that made a satisfying bulge on my chest wall, long before it came to resemble a breast. I feel that same satisfaction today, every time I look down at myself, put on a bra, or walk around in nightgown or T-shirt, assured of my symmetry. I am whole again. Not perfect, but whole.

During that long week before my surgery, there were a few upsetting forays outside the hermetic world of my illness. I went to a book party for a writer I knew, given by the publisher of her novel. It all seemed so bizarre, walking into the Greenwich Village bar carrying this enormous, life-shattering secret and having nowhere to put it. It was my first experience of alienation from the normal, healthy world, but by no means my last.

The people I knew there were not close friends, yet some part of me wanted to blurt out my bad news anyway, to relieve the sense of estrangement I felt. It was a little disconcerting to realize how close I was to responding to their polite, "How are yous," with the truth. There was anger and bitterness in that impulse, as if I wanted to assault them as I had been assaulted, to rub their faces in it. But I didn't, of course. I made a little polite, cocktail-party conversation, congratulated the author, and left.

The trip to Woodstock to visit my mother was difficult, as I had known it would be. I had witnessed her irrationality concerning all things medical before, and had more than an inkling of what to expect. Despite her own ill health, it was always a battle to get her to go to a doctor.

She was quiet while we filled her in about what had happened, until it came to the mastectomy. "That's the most ridiculous thing I ever heard of," she said angrily. "You're not going to let them do that to you, are you?"

Tom and I looked at each other.

My mother mentioned the friend of hers who'd had a mastectomy a dozen years ago. "They just lopped off her breast. Just cut it off. I think that's terrible."

"But it may have saved her life," I said.

"Oh, that's ridiculous. How could such a thing save her life?"

Tom patiently began to explain the rationale for the surgery. "Never mind," she said, waving him away. "I don't want to hear all that stuff."

Her upset about me was deflected into anger at my doctors, as if it were somehow their fault that I had cancer. For my mother, no treatment was the only good treatment.

Despite this, by the end of the week, as I approached the surgery, I felt calmer. I was sleeping again, with the help of pills. I was no longer reading voraciously at every opportunity, or obsessively calling my new women friends.

Because I had to, I'd made some sort of accommodation to my changed circumstances. That was hard to comprehend in itself. Was there no end to what people could live with? In between the tears and anxiety attacks, I actually felt quite strong.

Much of that strength I drew from Tom. He was always right there, reassuring me with his touch, reminding me of the possibility of rational thought when I became too distraught. As the week ended, and there was less to "do," we drew even closer, enclosed in our crisis.

The flashes of unreality—"Is this actually happening?"—were now accompanied by a sort of wonderment that Tom and I could go on with our lives, even in the face of this.

It seems odd to say this, but in those moments that weren't consumed with anxiety or grief, there was something absorbing, even romantic, about our predicament. Small things didn't matter anymore. Our moments together became precious. Our lovemaking took on a new poignancy.

On our last night at home before I was to go into the hospital, I found Tom in the living room, blankly staring at MTV. The song was "She Drives Me Crazy," by the Fine Young Cannibals. After a moment, I saw his shoulders shaking and realized he was sobbing.

"She drives me crazy, like no one else," the song's refrain went. "She drives me crazy, and I can't help myself."

My hospital room, while small, felt cozy and private. I knew I was fortunate that I could afford the single room, and a private duty nurse for two shifts after the surgery.

While Tom went to make phone calls, I laid out all my things, the teddy bear my Aunt Jo had given me, the frilly, high-necked nightgowns with easily-opening fronts I'd bought, my tapes and tape player. Soothing music helped with the pain, as I'd discovered when I'd had a hysterectomy six years before. I'd been assured that from a purely physical point of view, this surgery would be easier than that one, which had involved opening the abdomen. The pain would be far less, but I wanted to be prepared for it, nevertheless.

I plugged in the small reading lamp I'd brought, and turned out the harsh fluorescent overhead light. In the darkened room, I stood and looked at the lights of Manhattan spread out in the gathering dusk. It was a beautiful, clear evening, the pale violet of the twilight sky shading into a deep orange around the black cut-outs of skyscrapers.

Standing at the window, I had that same sense of clarity I'd felt at other turning points in my life, when change was imminent. Composed in equal parts of melancholy and anticipation, it was not an altogether bad feeling. Now that I was here and my decision was made, I would go with whatever happened, just give myself to the process, wherever it led.

I would be all right. That was what my surgeon had said. By now, I understood that his words, while kind, could not really predict my future. No one could. Still, like a child trustfully clinging to a comforting memory, I held them carefully in my mind.

With Tom snoring on the low cot beside me, I slept that night with my hand cupped protectively over my right breast. Dozing and waking, I watched as the sky became light. Before they came to take me in the early morning, I stood in the bathroom, with my hospital gown open, and looked at myself for the last time.

There are hallways, voices, elevator doors, punctuated by the sudden, sickening lateral movements of the gurney as I am pushed toward surgery. I am trying to keep my eyes open, but the heaviness of my eyelids makes it hard. I keep drifting and waking, squinting at the harsh lights overhead.

Suddenly, it gets much brighter.

"Okay, now," a woman's voice says. "We're going to move you now. Just scoot your hips over here."

I lie back on the operating table, dizzy from the effort, while they cover me again. I have arrived. The operating room is cold, but I am so relaxed from the preoperative medication they have given me that I barely register it.

I force my eyes open and look around, seeing the usual tools and machinery, the scrub nurses, the coldness of tiles and glass and gleaming metal. One of the nurses introduces herself.

"Now, what operation are we performing here today?" she asks, checking my plastic I.D. bracelet and jotting something down on a clipboard.

I tell her.

"And it's your right breast, is that correct?"

That wakes me up. I half sit up, alarmed. "You mean you don't know?"

"We have to check," she says, a calming hand on my arm. "This is just routine."

Dimly, I remember reading somewhere about a woman who'd actually had someone else's operation. These things do happen. Maybe I shouldn't be trusting all these strangers. "Where's my doctor?" I ask anxiously.

"Don't worry," she says. "He'll be in presently."

"Will I get to see him before they put me out?"

"Probably."

The anesthesiologist, a tall, gaunt figure in his green scrubs, looks down at me through wire-rimmed spectacles. Except for his voice with its soft, Middle-Eastern intonations, he does not at all resemble the charming professorial gentleman who stopped in my room the night before, with his Old World manners and three-piece suit.

Over the mask, his eyes crinkle in a smile. "I will wake you right after the surgery is done, before you go to the recovery room," he says. "You must try to remember what I tell you."

"Thank you," I murmur, feeling safe again.

I feel my arms being strapped down at right angles to my body, and a brief image of crucifixion crosses my fuddled mind. From far away, as if at the end of a long tunnel, I feel a vein in my hand being punctured.

And then the mask, and the darkness.

THREE
Risks and Regrets

Life can only be understood backwards,
but it must be lived forwards.
— SÖREN KIERKEGAARD

HANDS REACHED TOWARD me through the black fog and
roughly pulled me up into a sitting position, unleashing a surge
of nausea. Oh, God, did I feel awful. I struggled to lift my eyelids. Without my glasses, all I caught was a blurred glimpse of the recovery room, other beds, white- and green-suited attendants, the glint of machinery. A jacket of pain encased my chest and right arm. Something
hard and flat and cold pressed against my back for an interminable time,
and then I was released. The thought that this shouldn't be happening
lodged somewhere in my semi-consciousness, but I was still too drugged
to speak. I sank back into the darkness.

As soon as it was over, I forgot this enigmatic event as one forgets a
bad dream. It was not until five days later, when I was dressing to go
home from the hospital, that I discovered an X-ray in a large manila
envelope in the back of the closet in my room. No one seemed to know
what it was. I gave it to the nurse, thinking that the previous occupant
must have left it behind. But when she examined it, there was my name
and patient number, clearly emblazoned on one corner. I looked at the
ghostly rib cage and lungs on the thick film. Was that really me? I didn't
remember getting any chest X-ray.

"When was this taken?" I asked the surgical resident who had assisted
with my mastectomy, after he had finished with the discharge forms. He
was a quiet young man with a bad cold; that day he looked especially
exhausted and pasty-faced.

34

He glanced at the film and then at me, obviously hesitant to speak. "In the recovery room."

"What was wrong with me?" The fuzzy, unpleasant memory began to surface then, making a slow roll into consciousness, like some slimy monster of the deep.

"Nothing. The clamp count was off."

"What?"

"After surgery, we have to account for all the clamps and sponges and so forth."

"You're telling me you thought you'd actually left something inside me?" I said incredulously.

"No, no, it's just routine. We're required to do an X-ray, if the count is off."

Oh, great, I thought. Terrific. No wonder they hadn't told me. I was sorry I'd asked. Better not to have found out that I had been rudely jerked back to consciousness in the recovery room, then propped up to have a unnecessary dose of radiation, all for procedure's sake, because of some nurse or doctor's error.

I swallowed hard, and told myself to calm down. These things happen. Those three fatalistic words—how often had I heard them these last three weeks?

I held up the X-ray. "So what should I do with this?"

He shrugged. "Whatever you want."

I looked at the young doctor. He looked at me.

It wasn't his fault. No damage had been done. With all that had happened to me already, this just wasn't worth getting upset about. I'd be out of there in another hour, a free woman at last. But then what?

Most of the first day after surgery had been a blur. Drugged and in pain, I was only able to focus on just getting by, moment to moment. I do remember a few things: the gentle touch of the private duty nurse, arranging pillows so my chest and arm wouldn't hurt so much, the soothing sounds of Georgia Kelly and Paul Winter on my tape player, and, most of all, the simple relief that the surgery was over.

That first night, I felt well enough to make a few phone calls. In a moment of exhilaration, I even called the members of my longtime writing group, who were having their usual Monday night meeting. "I'm all right!" I crowed. They must have thought I was crazy, calling them at a time like that.

When the anesthesiologist stopped by my room that evening, I was in the middle of my first meal, attacking my Jello and apple juice with a ravenous appetite. I hadn't expected to see him.

He smiled at me. "Do you remember what I told you this morning, before you went into recovery?"

I shook my head. "It's all a blank until I came upstairs."

"What I told you was, your lymph nodes looked clear to me."

A wave of happiness passed through me, followed almost immediately by another, larger surge of doubt. "You can't tell from just looking, can you?"

"I don't believe I've ever been wrong. I do have a few years experience at this, you know."

"But I thought they didn't really know until—"

"Yes, of course, you'll have to wait for the pathologist's report to be one hundred percent certain. But I just wanted you to know that to me, your lymph nodes looked perfectly healthy."

Tom and I thanked him profusely, and he left.

"That's wonderful news," said Tom.

"Yes, but I'm afraid to believe him."

"Why?"

"What if he's wrong?"

Tom bent over me and stroked my hair. "He won't be. You're going to be fine."

Angry tears sprang to my eyes. "Don't tell me that."

I could see by the puzzled look on Tom's face that I had hurt his feelings. But in the ten days since my biopsy, avoiding nasty surprises had become more crucial to me than peace of mind that might prove temporary. Having some control over my experience assumed paramount importance, even if it meant dwelling on the worst possible outcome.

My brief exhilaration after the surgery came, at least in part, from the simple fact that it was over. I had survived. Regaining consciousness, I was able to pick up the continuity of my life, to once again follow the thread that links one moment to the next.

It was on the morning of the day after surgery that my dressing was changed and I saw my incision for the first time.

Thinking that the wide bandage that covered my chest would remain in place for at least a few days, I wasn't really prepared for this unveiling. Seeing oneself for the first time was supposed to be a dreadful trauma. I had read about women concealing their mastectomy scars from their husbands, and even from themselves, for weeks and months after the operation.

I looked up at the face of my plastic surgeon, who was carefully removing the adhesive tape that held the thick bandage they had placed on me after surgery.

"Should I look?" I asked.

"Sure," he said. "Why not?"

"I'm afraid."

"Oh, it's not so bad," he said. "It's a nice clean incision. You're flat, that's all."

I took a deep breath and gingerly looked down at my chest. There it was, or rather, there it wasn't. How strange. I waited to feel horrified, bereft, but I suppose my anticipation of those emotions had been so intense that the reality seemed strangely devoid of feeling.

Okay, I thought, I can handle this. It's not so terrible. The doctor's right: I'm just flat there, like a boy, or a child. I was somewhat appalled at the length of the incision, which snaked from the center of my chest all the way around back under my arm, but it wasn't repugnant to me.

The plastic surgeon placed a small gauze square over the site where two plastic tubes entered the skin to drain the wound, and left the incision uncovered.

"You're not going to bandage it again?" I asked.

"You don't need it," he told me.

After he had left the room, I unhooked myself from the wall suction that tugged painfully at the two tubes that entered my side, draining the wound, and shuffled into the bathroom. I raised my hospital gown and stared at my body in the mirror for a long time.

Bristling with stiff black threads from the tied sutures, a long puckered scar disappeared under my arm. Beneath the pectoral muscles, I could see the flat, oval outline of the tissue expander, which the plastic surgeon had implanted. Under the skin below my armpit was the small, round nub of the port through which saline solution would be injected.

Feeling suddenly faint, I held on to the edge of the sink. I kept on staring at myself, trying to come to terms with this newly lopsided person staring back at me from the mirror.

My relief of a few minutes earlier had dissipated, to be replaced with a stunned recognition of how profoundly and permanently I'd been changed. The longer I looked, the worse the asymmetry became. I thought of those circus freaks from my childhood, half man, half woman. I thought of what lay ahead, the months of saline injections, the additional surgeries. How could any plastic surgeon, however skilled, ever make me look or feel whole again?

My teeth began to chatter. I lowered myself, cautiously, to the toilet seat, and tried taking deep breaths. I sat there, hunched over, cradling my right elbow in my left hand. My chest and arm had begun to throb unbearably.

Doubts I thought I'd laid to rest before the surgery were back to haunt me. Had my decision to have a total mastectomy rather than a lumpectomy really been the right one? My surgery had involved removal of all breast tissue, including the skin and nipple, via a long, oval incision, after which the skin from above and below was joined. The extreme tightness under my arm, where the skin had been stretched to cover the lost flesh, was already apparent, as if I were wearing a badly tailored, ill-fitting suit. I could feel the painful pull on the sutures whenever I attempted to lift my arm.

It could be worse, I reminded myself. At least the muscles of my chest wall had been left intact. I could have been forced to undergo a radical mastectomy, which had at one time been the usual, and far more disfiguring, surgical treatment for breast cancer. Fifteen or twenty years ago, that was what would have happened to me.

On the other hand, I could have chosen a lumpectomy, and still have my breast. Feverishly, I went over and over the reasoning process that had led to my decision. If I'd elected to have a lumpectomy, I reminded myself, I'd have had to undergo five or six weeks of daily radiation treatments to my breast, in order to destroy any cancer cells that may have been missed. Radiation, like chemotherapy, had seemed to me like an extremity of another sort. Unlike surgery, whose effects were clear and unequivocal, radiation seemed mysterious, even menacing, with its invisible damaging rays.

The size and invasiveness of the tumor had also figured in my decision.

The small but significant risk of local recurrence with a lumpectomy might necessitate a later "salvage" mastectomy. The idea of going through all this again had seemed intolerable.

But the fact was, I could probably have kept my breast and learned to live with that anxiety. We adapt to our circumstances, whatever they are. *All* women with breast cancer worry about the future, but how much they worry seems to depend more upon personality than on what surgical procedure they've endured. Contrary to expectations, recent studies have found no greater degree of anxiety, over time, in women who have elected lumpectomy plus radiation than in women who've had mastectomies.

My hopes for reconstruction had played a large role in the choice I'd made. After seeing those slides my plastic surgeon had shown us, the loss of a breast seemed almost like a mere temporary inconvenience, like the renovation of an apartment—a mess while it's going on, but worth it, in the end.

Now, seeing how I actually looked, it was an altogether different matter. Even though the scar was neat, and clean, I looked—and felt—mutilated.

When my husband came in a couple of hours later, I was propped up in bed wearing my frilliest nightgown. I'd penciled my eyebrows and put on a little lipstick.

"They took off my bandage this morning," I told him, after he'd hung up his jacket and kissed me.

I watched his eyes flicker to the new flatness on the right side of my chest. "How was that?" he asked cautiously. "Did you look?"

"Yes."

"And?"

I rested my hand protectively over the spot. "Do you want to see?" I asked.

I watched the play of emotions across his face, the doubt, the fear, the wish to not hurt me with his response. He mustered his courage. "Sure," he said. "If you want me to. If you're ready."

I thought about that. Was I ready? Would I ever be more ready than I was at that moment? Probably not. Better to get this over with. The thought of sparing him, or concealing myself from him, never seriously occurred to me. I wanted him with me all the way, no secrets.

Untying the blue ribbon that bound the neck of the nightgown I was wearing, I thought ruefully of all the other times I had undressed for him, and how different this exposure was. I thought of how, two nights before, he had cradled my breast in his hand, and kissed it for the last time, as if saying goodbye, and we had both cried.

I unzipped the nightgown a few inches and folded the material back as he leaned over me. I watched his face, uncertain what I wanted or expected from him at that moment.

I longed to be told it made no difference, that he still desired me. Yet I knew how false this would be; I would never believe him were he to say this, at least not this soon. If losing my breast made such a difference to me, how could it fail to matter to him? No, I would want him to register the loss, to be devastated, just as I was.

I zipped myself up, retied the ribbons and tried a brave smile.

"The incision," he said, after a moment. "I had no idea it would be so long."

"Yeah, I know."

"But it's really not so bad," he said, and I could hear the surprise and relief in his voice. "Don't you think?"

"That was my first reaction, too."

He studied my face. "And then?"

I shook my head, and he reached out to stroke my cheek. This made the tears, which had been gathering all afternoon, spill down my face.

"Are you all right?" he asked.

Closing my eyes, I leaned my cheek against his hand and took a deep breath. "Yes."

"Sorry you showed me?"

I shook my head again. "I had to."

"Another hurdle."

"Yes," I said, "another hurdle."

But there were others still to come. The pathology report was the next.

This microscopic analysis would reveal the results of the axillary dissection procedure my surgeon had performed at the time of the mastectomy. Through an incision made under my right arm, he had "harvested" some thirty lymph nodes, which would each be examined microscopically for evidence of the spread of cancer from the primary tumor in my breast. The statistics in the text I'd read seemed to suggest that my chances of survival were strongly linked to the number of lymph nodes involved.

While there is certainly an increased risk for recurrence when the axillary lymph nodes show even microscopic evidence of cancer—especially if there are more than a few nodes involved—other factors, most of which have to do with the pathology of the particular cancer, are also important in determining prognosis. I didn't understand that then, nor could I have known the more recent findings that optimal adjuvant chemotherapy and hormonal treatment can save a majority of women with Stage II cancers. At the time, I had the mistaken, simplistic notion that cancer spread to the lymph nodes meant the difference between living and dying.

Like any other patient, I had to wait the customary four long days after surgery for the tissue removed to be analyzed. During this time, which seemed interminable, I tried to concentrate on my recovery, practicing the painful stretches that would eventually restore range of motion to my arm. The Reach to Recovery volunteer gave me a ball to squeeze and showed me how to stand facing a wall and climb up it with my fingers, an inch higher each time. But I was already climbing the walls, waiting.

At the same time, I felt pampered and cared for. There had been a tremendous outpouring of support from friends and family. My husband was beside me, bringing me delicacies from local delicatessens and Chinese restaurants in the neighborhood. For the first three nights, he slept in a cot beside my bed. I tried to think only of him and my sons, and of the cards and letters and flowers. I spent hours on the telephone.

There were the predictable post-surgical landmarks: the first time I could raise my arm over my head to wash my hair, my first shower, my first complete circuit of the halls. I learned how to unplug and empty my Hemo-Vac, the accordion-like suction device connected to the tubes draining my incision. I watered my flowers, which had, in their abundance, spilled over from the window ledge and were now crowding the available floor space. When I was able to get up and leave my room, I discovered on my return that it smelled like a hothouse. For those four days, the dread and anticipation I felt about the impending pathology

41

report hung as heavily in the air of my room as the dense and no longer entirely pleasant floral scent.

I was alone when I got the phone call. My surgeon was too elated, he told me, to wait for his customary afternoon rounds. "I have good news," he said. "Your nodes are clear."

The anxiety drained from my body, to be replaced by a giddy sensation of weightlessness. For the first time in the two weeks since the biopsy and my diagnosis, I felt a genuine sense of hope. Were it not for my sore chest and arm, I would have done a little dance of joy.

I was still trying to reach Tom at work an hour later when his eldest brother arrived. Because he taught in the medical school and was on staff at the hospital, Donald had been there to visit me every day. His knowledgeable support had been like a rock to which Tom and I had clung throughout my crisis. Though we had never discussed it, I knew that my condition must not have been easy for Donald because of the loss of his first wife to breast cancer a dozen years before.

I blurted out my good news. He turned away from me for a moment, and I realized that he was struggling to master his tears. Sandy's death was still there with us in the room.

That night, lying there in the semi-darkness and listening to the noises from the hospital corridor, I allowed myself to believe that I would live. It was the first time I had given myself the gift of that thought.

Six months or a year earlier, the fact that there was no cancer in my biopsied lymph nodes would probably have meant a reprieve from chemotherapy. But two months before my surgery, the results of three major studies, involving thousands of women, had been published in the *Journal of the American Medical Association*. The research indicated that even for those with no positive lymph nodes, adjuvant, or post-surgery, chemotherapy and/or hormonal therapy reduced the risk for recurrence of cancer by about ten percent—or, at least, it lengthened the time to recurrence. This finding led the National Cancer Institute to issue a clinical alert about the advisability of systemic treatment even for early-stage breast cancers.

Although my lymph nodes were negative, there were other factors which put me in a higher-risk category. My tumor had been large, about three centimeters, with poorly-defined margins, or edges, which suggested invasive tendencies. The size of the tumor meant that it had been growing in my breast for a longer period, perhaps as long as ten years. Clearly, there was some possibility of spread, depending on how well my immune system had been able to deal with any cancer cells breaking free and roaming around in the circulatory or lymphatic system.

All cancer is "staged" — a taxonomic system physicians use to describe the spread and severity of the disease — from Stage I, smallest and most localized, to Stage IV, which indicates measurable and established metastases elsewhere in the body. My cancer, although it had not spread to the lymph nodes, was considered Stage II, because of its size and invasiveness.

Even if the tumor had been considered Stage I, chemotherapy would still most likely have been recommended. Current thinking has overturned the old idea that cancer always spreads from one location throughout the body via the lymphatic system. Some early cancers appear to be systemic and invasive from the beginning, and therefore need systemic treatment that attacks all the rapidly dividing cells in the body, i.e., chemotherapy and/or hormonal therapy.

Other tumors seem to be completely localized, and, following local treatment, can be considered cured. This treatment usually consists of excisional surgery and/or radiation — in the case of breast cancer, mastectomy or lumpectomy with radiation.

The big problem here is that distinguishing one form of cancer from the other is frequently beyond the scope of current medical knowledge, although pathology can be of enormous assistance in this. The degree of disorganization of the cancer cells, a measure of DNA known as "ploidy," is an important prognostic indicator, for example. Cancer researchers have just begun to identify other substances, such as enzymes and growth factors, that may, ultimately, indicate who is most at risk for recurrence and can therefore benefit from the most aggressive treatment.

Where the tumor can be found to be ER-positive, meaning hormonally dependent (on estrogen and progesterone) for its growth, hormonal therapy — mostly commonly tamoxifen (Nolvadex), an estrogen-antagonist — is far less toxic than drugs like Adriamycin (doxorubicin), methotrexate, Cytoxan (cyclophosamide), and 5 fluorouracil (5-FU), four of the chemotherapeutic agents most commonly used for breast cancer when it is first diagnosed.

In the process of killing cancer cells, these cytotoxic agents also attack rapidly dividing cells in the body as a whole, including white blood cells in the bone marrow, gastric mucosa, hair follicles, and ovarian tissue. It is this scattershot action that causes the unpleasant and dangerous side effects of chemotherapy. It's like going after a flea with a baseball bat, to quote one graphic analogy.

In my case, the pathology report had shown that the cells of my breast cancer were not estrogen- or progesterone-receptor positive (ER-positive, for short), which meant that tumor growth was not strongly influenced by these hormones. The recurrence rate for ER-positive tumors is less than for ER-negative tumors, both because the cancer cells themselves show better differentiation, and because anti-estrogenic treatment is so effective in arresting the growth of these hormone dependent cancers.

Taking all this into consideration, my surgeon had referred me to an oncologist on the staff at the same medical center. "He's very sharp," the surgeon said. "The best we have here. I'll have him stop by to meet you before you leave the hospital."

I'm still not sure why my first meeting with that oncologist did not go well, or what it was about him that put me off. Certainly, his casual, even jocular attitude did not match my own worried mood. Nor did the offhanded way he launched into his explanation of the treatment he had planned for me, presenting it as if it were merely a little tidying-up after the mastectomy, no big deal. Perhaps he thought that an attitude of un-concern would be reassuring; I found it just the opposite. To me, chemotherapy *was* a big deal.

"Are these treatments going to make me really sick?" I wanted to know.

He shrugged. "They might. There's no way of predicting."

"Will I lose my hair?"

"Some do. Some don't. I always tell my patients to buy a wig before they start treatment." He looked at his watch and stood. "Call my office tomorrow. We'll get you started first thing next week."

After he left, I burst into tears. I had been so flustered that I hadn't even asked most of my questions.

Tom and I met again with this oncologist a few days after I'd left the hospital in his office at the faculty practice building. Following some meaningless chatter about the fact that we all lived on the Upper West

Side, I began asking questions from a written list we had made up together. This time I came prepared. I mentioned the studies I'd read. How were dosages determined, I wanted to know, and intervals between the cycles of injections? What were his beliefs about treating side effects? What about damage to the immune system?

The oncologist leaned back. "Let me tell you something," he said. "You're asking me about things that even the experts don't agree on. You're going to cause yourself a lot of grief if you try to second-guess us. Why don't you just sit back and let me make these decisions?"

"I'm sure that's okay for some people," Tom began.

The doctor sat forward in his chair. "Look," he said, gesturing in my direction, "this is not a sick lady. Her prognosis is pretty good—we're just gonna give her six treatments, and that's it."

I didn't care much for being talked about in the third person. "But you see, doctor, I do better with as much information as possible," I said, trying to keep my voice calm. "It makes me a whole lot less anxious."

His eyebrows shot up. "Oh, I doubt that. Most of my patients don't want to know all this stuff. That's what they pay me for."

It didn't seem worth arguing the point further, and we concluded the meeting and made an appointment the following Monday for my first treatment.

Tom turned to me when we left the office. "I don't like that man," he said. "How do you feel about him?"

"Well, his office staff seems nice," I said. "The nurses are the ones I'll be seeing, mostly."

"I don't care. I don't like him."

I knew I had to begin treatment soon, within the next week or two. The thought of finding another oncologist at this juncture was overwhelming. I'd already run that frantic round robin of second and third opinions in the ten days before my surgery. Besides, what would my surgeon, who had referred me to this oncologist, say? Would he be angry? Wouldn't there be problems if I went to another hospital, problems of communication and philosophy of treatment? At this point in my recovery, any hitch, however small, took on mammoth proportions.

But I also knew that Tom was right. With my fear of the chemotherapy, it was doubly important that I find someone I liked and trusted. This was a life-long relationship, as he pointed out.

"Okay, then you find me someone," I told Tom. "I can't deal with this." I could hear the petulance in my voice, but I couldn't help myself. All I wanted to do was to get home, lie down and go to sleep.

Many months later, I discovered that the oncologist to whom Tom and I had taken such an immediate dislike had cared for the mother of one of the women in my support group while she was dying of breast cancer. This same doctor that I found to be so flip and offhanded had apparently been a model of compassion for both the patient and her family. I kept my mouth shut about my own experience.

Perhaps, I thought then, with the benefit of time and the perspective it brings, my negative reaction had been a simple case of "kill the messenger." I was so petrified over the prospect of chemotherapy that I might have taken an active dislike to anyone who represented the treatment I so dreaded.

Throughout my treatment, I tried to contain my anger about what had happened to me and keep it from contaminating my relationships with the medical people who took care of me, since I was so dependent upon them. A targetless, helpless rage ran around and around inside me, building up a charge, seeking an outlet. The least infraction could release my pent-up wrath. In the end, though, there was no one to blame; it was no one's fault I had cancer.

Accepting the fact that I had to undergo chemotherapy was one of the most difficult hurdles of all to face, harder in many ways than the mastectomy. Like many people, I thought of the drugs oncologists used as poisons. I had heard and read about the side effects of these toxic chemicals, as we all have, and I imagined myself enervated, hairless, desperately sick. How would I manage to get through it?

The medical texts and articles I'd read only heightened my anxiety by adding a few more side effects I hadn't been aware of—the really dangerous ones, like bone-marrow suppression. Two recently published books, offered by a well-meaning friend, told the usual "chemo" tales of harrowing reactions to the drugs, reactions so severe that completing the course of treatment had been difficult, and in one case impossible. Highly dramatized scenes of hours and days spent kneeling on the bathroom floor, retching blood, did nothing to calm my fears.

What helped enormously during those weeks of waiting were my telephone conversations with others who had undergone similar treatments.

I found each of these women by chance, through an informal network of friends of friends. Like a new patch sewn on a warm quilt, each conversation seemed to supply just the kind of information and comfort I needed at the moment.

What these new friends had to say was reassuring. The side effects of chemotherapy, while unpleasant, were hardly as awful as I imagined. Sure, they felt more tired than usual, at least on the days right after the treatments. But there were medications to deal with the nausea, and an awful lot of hair could be lost before a wig was needed. There were tricks with scarves and short haircuts. Throughout their treatment, these women had continued to exercise, travel, work, and take care of their families. One of them, with considerable pride, boasted that no one at her job had even known about her chemo!

Some months later, when I joined a support group for breast cancer patients, these experiences with chemotherapy were confirmed by almost all the women there, including, by that time, myself.

Why, then, was this less extreme picture not reflected in what I'd read? Several factors are at work, I believe.

In the public mind, chemotherapy is a unified, singular experience. This is not the case. There are a number of different drugs and combinations of drugs used for breast cancer. Each has different effects and side effects; each woman responds differently. Some cytotoxic drugs used in advanced disease (secondary and tertiary treatment) are far more debilitating than those used for primary treatment. Usually, the dosage and toxicity of the drugs used in adjuvant treatment determines the severity of side effects, although not invariably.

Adriamycin, in particular, causes nausea and vomiting in as many as half the women to whom it is administered. And it invariably leads to almost complete hair loss. Because it is the most potent as well as the most toxic of the chemicals used in primary or adjuvant treatment, this drug, which also carries a risk of damaging the heart, is often reserved for women with more advanced disease, whose cancer has already spread to the lymph nodes. Cytoxan, methotrexate and fluorouracil, the other three commonly used drugs in breast cancer—called "CMF" when administered together—generally have less severe side effects, at least in eighty percent of the women who take them.

Some of the first-person accounts I'd read of chemotherapy involved higher-dosage treatments for more advanced disease, which is not the experience the majority of women facing chemotherapy for breast cancer can expect. The side effects of these more aggressive treatments can be difficult, although not invariably so. A number of women have told me that they sailed through treatment with Adriamycin with no major problems.

One intriguing research study, done at Memorial Sloan-Kettering Cancer Center in New York, shows that "non-pharmacologic factors" — i.e., patient expectations and heightened anxiety — contribute far more to post-treatment nausea than does the dosage or kind of drugs administered. "Patient expectations establish self-fulfilling prophecies," the researchers conclude, "which contribute to the intensity of the side effects experienced."

In the same way and for the same reasons that cancer equals death in the public mind, chemotherapy has come to equal abject suffering. While we may accept the idea that half of those with cancer survive, it is the deaths that we remember and that engage our emotions. Surviving is a private act that occurs quietly, over many years. Survivors disappear into the crowd at large; in time, we forget they've even been ill.

Those who endure chemotherapy without much fuss are likewise invisible. They are not the ones we remember.

Further confusing the situation seems to be a certain amount of braggadocio on the part of those who have been through the experience. I understand this only too well. During and even after I was done with my treatment, I too felt an urge to "awfulize." This impulse to exaggerate our misfortunes seems to be a universal human trait. It doesn't seem so very wrong to use a little hyperbole to extract needed sympathy and respect for one's ordeal from others.

As for what appears in print, the heightened drama of severe side effects must make for more suspenseful reading. Fifteen hours of projectile vomiting is likely to be more interesting to the reader than fifteen hours of flu-like malaise. Perhaps the minority of women who encounter such miseries feel more drawn to write about them later. The rest of us, with nothing more to report than just dragging around, feeling out of sorts, never get to tell our boring "war stories."

But they must be told. Any lessening of the dread most women feel about chemotherapy is bound to send us into treatment sooner, when the disease is potentially curable—and keep us there long enough to get the maximum benefit.

My surgeon and oncologist both claim that the majority of women they see with breast cancer are unnecessarily terrified at the prospect of receiving chemotherapy; that they fear it more than mastectomy, and in many cases, even more than the cancer itself.

"In the minds of most women I see," my oncologist told me, "adjuvant treatment is still associated with advanced disease and death. If they have to have chemotherapy, it means they're in big trouble. It's hard for them to see it positively, as life-giving."

For the woman in treatment, a downward spiraling cycle of events is easily established, where apprehension leads to intensified side effects, which in turn lead to greater fears, and so forth. Much unnecessary suffering, emotional and physical, is caused by negative expectations before and during treatment.

This vicious cycle may eventually lead to the interruption of therapy. A study in *The New England Journal of Medicine*, on physical and psychological distress associated with chemotherapy, found that women receiving CMF experienced "only mild physical distress," but came to the conclusion that, "Psychologic reactions rather than physical toxicity may lead to discontinuing adjuvant therapy."

These attitudes do not begin with diagnosis. They are part of the culture at large. "I wish we could stop using the term 'chemotherapy' altogether in cancer treatment," my oncologist said. "After all, we don't refer to heart medications as chemotherapy, yet they are, as much as any of the drugs I use."

When it comes to breast cancer, it seems that ignorance, misinformation, and fear are intimately connected. At the time of my diagnosis, I was woefully ignorant about breast cancer, despite my regular mammograms and previous biopsies.

The early onset of my menstruation, at age eleven, as well as the fibrocystic changes in my breasts, may have put me at slightly higher risk for breast cancer. The most significant risk factors for breast cancer are clearly age and sex, experts feel. While there are probably many other co-factors, known and unknown, that contribute to the development of the disease, the actual significance of these factors is more speculative than factual. Once researchers determine where the genetic mutation occurs, they will be able to link the incidence of breast cancer with that of other potential risks.

Because my father had died of a heart attack at sixty-six, and my mother had suffered a stroke, I'd assumed that where heredity was concerned, my cardiovascular system was my weak link. This may still prove to be the case, should I live long enough. But I'd had my children early, and there was no history of cancer in my family—that is, until my mother was diagnosed as having breast cancer at eighty-one, four months after my mastectomy led her to examine her breasts for the first time in her life.

There are so many things that I wish I had known.

No one bothered to tell me, for example, that my mammograms were virtually unreadable—the word was "uninformative"—owing to the density of the breast tissue. I didn't know then that this is often the case in premenopausal women, especially those with fibrocystic changes or benign breast disease—not a real disease at all, but a common condition involving cysts, dense breast tissue, fibroadenomas or just plain lumpy breasts, usually fluctuating with monthly hormone levels and affecting a large minority of menstruating women.

I assumed that a negative mammography report meant the radiologist had seen the lump and decided it was not a problem. I didn't know about the rate of false negatives for mammography, which can run as high as fifteen to twenty percent, even if the mammogram is properly done, which is not always the case. I never knew that qualitative differences in mammograms could be significant, and that some films are of such poor quality as to be worse than worthless.

I never even thought to question my gynecologist's dismissive attitude when I first brought the lump to his attention. "Don't worry about it," he'd said offhandedly. "It's only a cyst."

God knows that was what I wanted to hear, and I left his office that day enormously relieved, unaware that I had just entered into a collusion with him that would have dire consequences. This, I told myself, was a sophisticated, knowledgeable doctor who could tell about breast lumps just from feeling them, someone far more competent than the young Ohio surgeon who had botched that last biopsy and sent me home still hemorrhaging inside the stitched-up incision.

I was in New York City now, getting world-class medical attention,

I assured myself. This was a kind, considerate physician, a man who had performed a hysterectomy on me five years earlier and whom I trusted with childlike adoration.

That blind trust, combined with misinformation and my own capacity for denial, had delayed my biopsy for more than a year. Whether that year's delay would have made an important difference in prognosis or treatment is impossible to say, but it well might have. I might still have my breast. I might not have had to receive chemotherapy. Awful as it is to contemplate, that delay may ultimately cost me my life.

If only. The two saddest words in my vocabulary, these past two years.

Embittered, I never spoke to this doctor again after my mastectomy. I didn't know then that failure to diagnose breast cancer has become one of the leading grounds for malpractice suits in this litigious age, and that this charge results in the largest financial settlements, each averaging about $200,000, according to a recent study by the Physician Insurers of America.

I simply assumed my situation was unique, or at least uncommon. Some months later, I was stunned to find that in my support group of eleven, *eight* reported similar experiences with their gynecologists. One has since successfully taken legal action. The rest, I imagine, think about doing so. I know I have.

When I spoke to my brother-in-law, a general surgeon himself, about what had happened to me, I could see his hackles rise at the accusation of malpractice contained in my question. "If we were to biopsy every breast lump we found," he told me, "they'd be doing nothing else in operating rooms. We have to make choices."

Another illusion gone. Caveat emptor. If my own brother-in-law would rise to the defense of this gynecologist he didn't even know, I knew I couldn't expect to be taken care of anymore. It wasn't just a matter of finding a better doctor, one who would be more cautious and thorough.

There was another, larger issue to consider here. I was playing an altogether different game now, and with higher stakes, than the physicians I consulted. However individualized their attention appeared to be, however specific their sense of my particular case, in their own minds they were always comparing me with the aggregate, making educated guesses based on statistical probabilities. How could it be otherwise?

I, on the other hand, had only myself to consider. If I needed an advocate, it would have to be me. It was *my* lump, *my* cancer, and *my* life that was at stake.

Part of the regression that often accompanies illness involves a tendency to see the doctor as an idealized and trusted parent, to whom the patient turns for healing, advice, and the power to make everything better.

The serious distortion of this view contributes mightily to the malpractice boom in this country. It causes people to expect god-like powers from their physicians, who are then punished for not being able to heal all ills. It causes patients to become passive, putting themselves in the hands of these all-knowing, all-seeing doctors, when what they should be doing is consulting them and then weighing what they are told against their own informed judgments.

With time and genuine caring, a true healing partnership is possible. Like every other human relationship, this demands mutual respect, consideration, and honesty. It depends on trust built over years of experience. Of course, this requires considerable effort on the part of both doctor and patient. But for me, this kind of partnership has been invaluable, particularly with my oncologist, but also with my two surgeons.

Still, for the most part, the physicians I've consulted, even the best of them, are simply too busy to keep track of much beyond the immediate crisis at hand. Because doctors rarely have the time to inform their patients adequately, we are often forced to research our illnesses ourselves. Although I'm not trained to interpret what I read, I make sure to look up every medication I take in the *Physician's Desk Reference*. When I go in for my checkups, it is always with a list of questions in my purse.

I do a lot of prompting when I go to a doctor's office. Did the results of this or that test come in yet? Is the doctor aware of allergies, other medications, or any confounding circumstances? Such vital information must be volunteered. What isn't written in one's chart in plain view may not be remembered and taken into account. Often, our body parts and organ systems are parceled out among different physicians. The person with a serious illness that spans several medical specialties soon discovers how difficult it is to coordinate care and communication among the various doctors who may be involved.

In a pioneering study done at King's College Hospital in London and published in 1979, British psychiatrist H. Steven Greer assessed women's psychological responses to breast cancer three months after diagnosis, and then looked at the outcome five and ten years later. After ten years, he discovered that fifty-five percent of patients who had initially reacted to cancer with denial or who had demonstrated a fighting spirit, were alive and disease-free, while only twenty-two percent of patients who had responded with stoic acceptance or feelings of helplessness or hopelessness were still free of cancer. Initially, these four groups had been matched in all other meaningful criteria, including stage of cancer.

Other well designed research has been able to link disease-free survival with such factors as extroversion and social support, and poor prognosis with repression, an attitude of helplessness and hopelessness, social isolation, and severely stressful life events.

Some studies of newly diagnosed breast cancer patients followed over time have also suggested that those women who are the most demanding, assertive and participatory with regard to their treatment tend to live longer. Far from being "good patients," these uppity ladies complain, get angry, and question everything done to them. They ask to have procedures explained. They want second and third and fourth opinions. They want to read and understand their own charts and reports. They carry around medical journals and cite references to their exasperated physicians.

These women may give nurses and doctors a hard time, and they may not win popularity contests, but they seem to do better medically. Whether this is simply because these "squeaky wheels" receive better treatment because they insist on it, or whether there is actually something biologically protective about this sort of personality, is anyone's guess.

Although I've learned to assert myself more these last two years than ever before in my life, I can never quite muster up that necessary sense of entitlement that I sometimes observe in other women. This attitude evokes both a grudging admiration and a certain residual feeling of distaste on my part. My natural tendency—against which I struggle daily— is to defer to authority and avoid causing a commotion.

However, as we all come to realize sooner or later, the world is well-populated with incompetence and lack of consideration. Hospitals are notoriously Byzantine institutions. Even with the best of medical care, anyone with a serious illness is bound to encounter her share of nasty receptionists, lost records and reports, clumsy technicians, harried nurses, unconscionably long waiting periods, and so forth.

And these are only the commonplace, everyday occurrences, the minor annoyances. I suspect that many women who have been through the ordeal of breast cancer have, like me, another, darker list, of truly unforgivable moments at the hands of the medical bureaucracy.

When my support group made the disturbing discovery that most of us had been lulled into a false and potentially fatal sense of security by our gynecologists, there was one notable exception among our ranks.

"He told me not to be concerned about the lump, but I was," Rosa said simply. "It still bothered me. So I decided to do something about it." It was her insistence on a biopsy, against her doctor's recommendations, that led to an early diagnosis. As a result, this young woman did not have to undergo chemotherapy, and her prognosis is now excellent.

Still, that timid child within me squirms with embarrassment for an uneasy moment before she can bring herself to speak up for herself.

But I am learning.

All I have to do is remember that X-ray in the back of the closet of my hospital room.

FOUR

Upside-Down World

My world is upside down, and I do not know what
will survive from this strange new knowledge.
— DOROTHEA LYNCH
Exploding into Life

Y OU'RE SURE YOU'RE up to this?" Tom winced as he watched me
trying to slide my dress over my head without raising my right
arm. "We could wait until next week, you know."

"I'm all right. Really." Under the dress, I adjusted the flesh-colored
breast form, with its puff of fiberfill, that the Reach to Recovery volunteer had given me. It was now attached with two tiny safety pins to one
of Tom's worn cotton undershirts.

The undershirt was all I could tolerate against my skin. Even though
it made me look more "normal," the pressure of the tight surgical bra
against my healing incision was torment. Comfort took precedence over
appearance. I turned to face him. "How do I look?" I asked.

I had wanted us to celebrate our wedding anniversary by going out
for dinner. It was our thirteenth—a lucky number, I insisted, against all
evidence to the contrary. I wasn't about to let anything stand in the way
of observing the occasion, even though I'd only been home from the
hospital for two days and was still weak and in pain. I'm not sure Tom,
or any of my family or friends, for that matter, knew how to respond
to my fierce determination to maintain ritual and relationships just as
they had been before.

Joining us that evening at the Café des Artistes were Donald, his wife
Carol, and my old friend Faith, who had come from California to be
with me for a few days when I first came home from the hospital. A bot-

tle of champagne was ordered; a toast was made. Taking their cue from me, the others relaxed and began to act as if this were just another night out in a restaurant. I smiled and drank and made conversation, as if to say, look, here we all are and nothing's changed.

At one point, Carol leaned over to me. "I don't know how you're doing this," she whispered. "If it were me . . . " She shook her head.

"Oh, you'd rise to the occasion, too," I replied. "What else is there to do?"

"I think I'd just fold up and crawl into bed and not want to see anyone."

"You know, it's strange," I said. "Something minor can really lay me low. But this, it's as if it's too large. I feel as if I have to hold it together. I can't give in to it."

"Well, I think you're just terrific."

I thanked her, gratified at the compliment. I was trying on for size a new role that night: the brave, uncomplaining—at least, to the outside world—cancer patient. So far, so good.

But as the evening wore on, my resolve faltered. Although I'd had only one glass of wine, I found I couldn't focus on the conversation. I began to feel as if the others were drifting out of my reach, and were far away, comfortably ensconced in the noisy and oblivious world of the healthy. In the hospital, at least, I'd had a place, an identity; here, I felt lost. I couldn't seem to find a spot to rest my right elbow; the weight of my arm pulled relentlessly against the incision. The combination of pain and wine was making me faint.

Evidently, I wasn't going to be able to tough it out. An effort of will would not suffice tonight. That thin veneer of courage, bravado, and plain foolishness was about to crack. The restaurant was crowded; heat and chatter surrounded us, and I began to wonder if I would be able to stand up and walk when we left.

Since I was obviously not well, the meal was abbreviated. Coffee was hurriedly drunk and the bill paid. Our guests seemed relieved at the opportunity to resume their solicitous behavior. "Don't be silly," they replied, when I apologized.

Back in bed at home, I was miserable. My incision throbbed like a second, dark heart on the other side of my chest, punishing me for the evening's pretense of normalcy. I felt trapped in a maimed body. It was tolerable to think that this feeling would be with me, every moment of the day and night, until I healed.

Tom tried to comfort me. "I'm sorry, I'm so sorry," I kept blubbering, not knowing what I was apologizing for—my tears, the ruined evening, the cancer, or all of it, balled into one great miserable soggy mass.

I was starting to feel a tremendous sense of guilt for putting Tom through all this. It wasn't my fault I had cancer, and I knew he didn't blame me for it. Yet I still felt responsible.

He felt even more helpless than I did. His work, his own needs, all of his daily existence had just been swept aside by this crisis. I was the one receiving the cards and phone calls and flowers. I was the one friends asked about. Yet he suffered, too.

Since my diagnosis, I had been consumed with my predicament, with barely a thought for Tom's well-being. Even now, at this moment, he was having to sit there and comfort me, again, as he had so often these last few weeks. He wouldn't feel better until I did, and who knew when that would be?

The thought that I had now lost both my uterus and one of my breasts unleashed a new flood of tears. How could Tom go on loving me like this? Too many of my parts were missing. Damaged goods, that's all I was now. I didn't feel female anymore, much less like a sexual being.

"I'm sorry. I'm so sorry." Months later I read that those had been Nancy Reagan's first words to her husband, after her mastectomy.

My self-involvement didn't make me feel deserving, however. Although I longed for it, I was lousy at letting myself be cared for. My friend Faith kept having to remind me to get back into bed, to rest. Whenever she did something for me, I would jump up and try to help out.

Meanwhile, Tom had managed to find an oncologist for me, a personable and literate man, well respected in his field, who ran his own research foundation at one of the other major cancer centers in New York City.

To my relief, I learned that the treatments would be administered not in a hospital clinic but in his private office, a much less formidable setting. The regimen of drugs he recommended was similar to that which the other oncologist had discussed with us, but more intensive. For the first six weeks, I'd take Cytoxan orally three times a day, and have weekly injections of methotrexate and 5 fluorouracil. After that I would have three or four weeks off to rebuild my white blood count, then injections of all three drugs every two weeks, for a total of thirteen or fourteen cycles over a sixth-month period.

For the first six weeks, I'd also be taking prednisone, a corticosteroid that would help to minimize the side effects of the other drugs, and that was in itself cytotoxic—it killed cancer cells.

"Sometimes people have trouble sleeping with the prednisone," he warned me. "It makes them a little euphoric."

That didn't sound so bad to me. I could use a little euphoria, I thought.

After spending a morning reviewing my pathology report with the oncologist, and listening to his recommendations, I scheduled my first chemotherapy session for the following Friday.

As I was about to leave his office, the doctor motioned me into one of the examining rooms. "Would you be interested in speaking with one of my breast cancer patients who has just completed her treatment?"

Of course I would, I told him. I'd be delighted. Though I'd liked this doctor's manner before, and had trusted his competence, it was this simple act in recognition of my emotional needs that endeared him to me the most.

The woman and I sat in a small unused office and talked. She had come in that day for her quarterly checkup and was clearly elated that it was over and that she showed no evidence of recurrence. Losing her hair had been the worst part of her chemotherapy, she confided, then smiled at me as she ran her fingers through her short curly mane. "It's true, what they tell you, you know," she said.

"What's that?"

"That it all grows back, thicker than ever."

The day before I was to have my first chemotherapy treatment, I attended my graduation ceremonies at Columbia University, where I was to receive an M.F.A. degree from the Writing Division of the School of the Arts. I had finished my coursework some months before, and handed in my thesis, a novel, only a few weeks before my diagnosis. No one at Columbia had known of my illness. I hadn't felt close enough to anyone there to call them before my surgery.

As I stepped up on the stage and accepted my diploma from the department chairman, I was possessed by the strangest feeling that this was some sort of transition, and not an ending. School wasn't really out, after all. I was, in a sense, moving from one identity to another. The change from student writer to cancer patient seemed merely another kind of graduation to a new and more demanding post-graduate level of study. For three years, I had worked hard at that. Now I would work hard at this.

True, I hadn't chosen cancer as I had chosen to go to graduate school, but it was the central fact of my life now, to do with as I saw fit.

It occurred to me that this business of having cancer could be viewed as a sort of project, or task, to be undertaken, rather than as a terrible blow to which I had fallen victim. In the few days since I'd been home from the hospital, I had begun investigating imagery and meditation instruction, massage, support groups, dietary consultants. Nothing too far out. But I could see already that I would need help coping with all of this emotionally, beyond what individual therapy might offer.

The twin illusions of safety and time had been early casualties of my cancer. Without even realizing it, before my diagnosis I had been living in an open, expansive interior space. Now the walls and ceilings had moved uncomfortably close. Limits were everywhere I looked: limits to health, strength, to life itself. Gone was my sense of feeling protected or secure. Gone, too, was any feeling of certainty about the future. As my treatment progressed, these invisible losses were to become more painful, in some ways, than the outward, physical losses and privations of the disease and its remedies.

The notion that I could do something beyond being the passive recipient of treatment calmed me. As the days went by, I found myself drawn toward the possibility of turning adversity into something I could use, something that might be of real value in my life.

This was one illusion I was not willing to throw on the scrap heap with the others. I refused to accept the idea that this terrible event had happened for no reason, and to no purpose.

While a part of me cherished the solicitous attention I received from others, I could not accept myself as a cancer "victim." Victim meant powerless, weak, to be pitied; someone to whom things just happened.

Yet, I couldn't deny the disturbing, oddly exalted feeling that I had somehow been singled out by this disease. I wasn't sure why yet, but I had the clear feeling that I'd been chosen. By whom, or for what, I couldn't begin to imagine. At times, I experienced what can only be described as a distinct sense of imminence, as if some profound meaning was about to be revealed to me. The word "challenge" crept into my vocabulary. I began to copy inspirational epithets into my journal, quotes like: "There is nothing the body suffers which the soul may not profit by," and, "What does not destroy me, makes me strong."

I can see now that this feeling of being chosen was actually another form of victimization, but turned upside down—a paranoid perception, reframed in positive terms.

At the time, I suspected that some state of post-surgical psychosis or traumatic stress might be generating these potent new thoughts. And I hadn't even begun taking the prednisone, which my oncologist claimed would make me euphoric. Oh boy, I thought, I'm going to be flying!

I felt uneasy revealing these feelings of transcendence to the therapist I'd been seeing when I was diagnosed. Despite our work together, I sensed a certain estrangement in our sessions. I was in another world now, a world he could not possibly enter with me. Fearful that he would caution me about being grandiose, or confront me over my reluctance to admit my vulnerability, I marshaled my defenses. I wasn't really manic, was I? How could something that felt so good be pathological?

With neither the inclination nor the energy to analyze this process, I simply turned elsewhere. Of course, I was well aware of how my therapist would feel about my "splitting the transference"—by which he meant I shouldn't expose myself to other, competing ideas and treatments. I didn't care. If unadorned reality was all he had to offer me, I just wasn't that interested.

My graduation from Columbia was not the only transition in my life. In fact, I'd been at loose ends for some time. Six months before, my first book had been published, a memoir about my father. *Night Studio* had turned out to be as much autobiography as biography, and its publication had left me feeling exposed, both as a writer and as the daughter of a well-known artist.

The book was widely reviewed because of its subject. By revealing myself so openly, I had taken a risk, had weathered the judgments of others and learned how to stand before an audience and speak without fear. There had been interviews and readings, and many warm letters from my father's former students and admirers of his painting.

The whole process, from beginning to end, had been a gratifying, if at times anxiety-producing, experience. Though I had come late to my craft, I finally believed that I could have a life as a writer.

But this book was a tough act to follow. At the time of my diagnosis, I had given up my attempts at revising the novel I'd been working on for several years, and had handed it in as my master's thesis. I'd been traveling in Europe with two major exhibitions of my father's work, and trying to decide what came next.

Cancer made that decision for me.

Those who see disease as deriving from the total fabric of a person's life, rather than from meaningless cellular mishap, will undoubtedly find significance in this. I did, for a time. It was one of many interpretations I considered during this strange period when I became obsessed with searching for causes, and toyed with alternative treatments.

At the same time, I was skeptical about that glib school of thought that reinterprets all unanticipated miseries of life as "learning experiences." That phrase had always made me groan. Oh, dear, I thought, was having cancer going to turn me into some California-style, New Age aficionado? I had flirted with such ideas during other difficult times in my life. Would I now become a closet Pollyanna?

I stood there among my fellow students at the graduation, bearing a secret beneath my blouse, a profound bit of knowledge that I knew would change, that had already changed, my whole life.

At the reception afterward, I told a few faculty members and students about my surgery, taking a certain satisfaction in the cautious respect I saw in their faces after their first shocked reactions, when they realized how recent my mastectomy had been. "Two weeks!" they all said. "But you look so well!"

They were responding to their own expectations of what a cancer patient should look like, I'm sure, as well as to the twenty pounds I had lost in the three months before my diagnosis. I did look good, but it was more than just the weight loss. I felt triumphant that day, clear-headed and wise. I was going to beat this thing, and meet the challenge heroically.

"A dangerous illness fills you with adrenaline and makes you feel very smart," wrote Anatole Broyard about his prostate cancer. "Suddenly, there was in the air a rich sense of crisis, real crisis . . . "

This was no longer a matter of struggling with my insecurities. Garden-variety neurotic conflicts crumbled into insignificance when the stakes were this high—temporarily, at least. This struggle was "real," and it was mortal. After the initial shock and grief, I found myself almost welcoming the sense of "real crisis," for the way it gave rise to immediate feelings of enlargement and purpose, after such a long, dry spell. The imperative of illness had a way of making things wonderfully clear.

Many people find that after the first storm of emotion has passed, there is a certain liberation in having a life-threatening disease. A sort of psychic spring-cleaning occurs. Social obligations and the need to please others come to seem trivial. Long-repressed emotions are allowed their expression, for good or for ill. Bad marriages end; good marriages become more intimate. Things of importance can no longer be postponed. Things of little consequence are no longer worth pursuing. Unrealized life-wishes, shoved aside from caution or timidity, reassert themselves.

In those first months, dealing with cancer was like body-surfing. A big wave might smash me down against the hard sand with terrible force, or simply leave me floundering in its backwash. But if I could somehow manage to catch that surge just right, as it was cresting, the force of it moved me within it, propelled in a kind of fluid harmony.

It was an exhilarating but short-lasting ride. Most of the time, I found myself just paddling around, waiting for something to happen, shivering and wishing I could get out of the cold water, back on *terra firma*.

Like it or not, I was a cancer patient now. A new way of being and doing was necessary. As Gertrude Stein once said, "You have to learn to do everything, even to die."

But it's a complicated affair, this sort of learning, and there are few realistic models. Formal instruction and an organized curriculum do not accompany life's major hurdles. I had to learn how to be ill, and then how to be well again and move on with my life. It was first a body of knowledge to be absorbed, then a series of procedures to be undertaken, and then finally a complex of emotions to be reckoned with. And this was just the beginning. I still had chemotherapy ahead of me.

One of my first forays out into New York by myself after my surgery had been down to Greenwich Village, to a New Age bookstore. The bumps over potholes and sudden stops of a taxicab ride would have been too painful with my healing incision, so I took the subway. I can clearly recall how vulnerable I felt, entering that crowded car, holding my right arm protectively away from my body to avoid getting jostled by the people around me.

At the bookstore, the glass cabinet by the checkout counter was filled with crystals and incense. An Indian raga was playing. Feeling slightly embarrassed, like a kid buying condoms, I purchased an audiotape with the decidedly hokey title, "An Answer to Cancer." Oh, well, I thought. At least it isn't claiming to be *the* answer to cancer.

When I was recovering from surgery, the closed-circuit TV channel in my hospital room had been playing a continuous videotape of relaxation instruction with soft music. I had used it more than once, and found it surprisingly helpful with the pain. Each time I listened to the tape, it left me in a serene, calm state that lasted for as long as an hour or two.

To my surprise, I liked the tape I had bought. The melodious voice of a California psychologist led the listener through a progressive relaxation procedure and then a visualization. The patient was asked to imagine the chemotherapy as a warm golden liquid, energizing the body, attacking the cancer cells. My mind's eye filled with elaborate images. My circulatory system became a labyrinth of ridged, interconnected tunnels through which a honey-like substance flowed while hordes of small, red, disc-like creatures ricocheted off the walls. White cells floated by, trailing diaphanous veils. I grasped at an image for the cancer and came up with a faint gray patch, like a mold, on the side of one of the tunnels.

At this point, I lost the image altogether as my body became rigid with tension. Fifteen years before, I'd read a book by Dr. O. Carl Simonton, a Texas radiation oncologist, and his wife Stephanie Matthews Simonton, a therapist, entitled *Getting Well Again*. Through visualization, they believed, one could learn to influence actual processes within the body, and thereby gain control over the course of the illness.

But if these mind-body techniques were as effective as their proponents claimed them to be, did I run the risk of actually invoking cancer by visualizing it, or by entertaining the belief that it was still there? After all, there was a good chance, better than fifty-fifty, that the mastectomy had removed all the cancer from my body. Was it denial to think that I might be—dare I even think the word—cured?

During this time, I was filled with superstitious thoughts, vacillating from utter helplessness to omnipotent fantasies that I might destroy myself with such innocent weapons as daydreams and beliefs.

What about chemotherapy? By submitting myself to the treatment, I was, in a sense, actually betting on the possibility that I might not be cured, that the worst might happen. It was like buying insurance, wagering on catastrophe. If beliefs could kill or heal, weren't some beliefs dangerous, in and of themselves? Surely that was implied in what I was doing. Perhaps I was subtly acknowledging—some might say actually *inviting*—the cancer back, through my beliefs about needing chemotherapy.

I couldn't make sense of any of this. The logical inconsistencies were irresolvable. While I wanted to "do it all," to investigate anything and everything, within reason, that might help me get well, I wasn't sure what to do with questions of logic and common sense. Given my analytical mind, how was I to cope with contradictory theories and ideas? I couldn't make that leap of faith these techniques appeared to require, nor could I figure out a way to sort out the genuinely helpful from the frivolous and misleading and downright harmful.

Were it not for a recommendation from someone I trusted, I would never have gone to visit the glamorous lady who specialized in autohypnosis and guided imagery. With her blond hair piled up on her head, her high-heeled slippers and elaborate make-up, she looked more like a fading actress than someone who could help me. Amid the rubbings and masks and exotic carvings in her Upper West Side apartment, I dutifully performed the prescribed breathing exercises until I felt light-headed. Inhale through the right nostril to the count of twenty, hold for ten, then exhale through the left nostril to the count of thirty. With my eyes closed, I let her suggest to me that I would transform the physical sensations of chemotherapy to ones that were actually pleasurable. Nausea would be perceived as hunger; tiredness would become pleasant relaxation.

I was encouraged to ask for a "friend," a fantasy companion who would comfort me. Thinking of the teddy bear my aunt had given me to take to the hospital, I was immediately visited by a vision of a human-sized, rather scraggly-looking but sweet tempered bear named Willy, who bore a decided resemblance to the growling, benign Chewbacca of *Star Wars* fame. Willy proceeded to enfold me in his arms, and we began—of all things—to dance a slow foxtrot.

"Good," the glamorous lady told me when I reported this. "Willy will always be there, whenever you need him." For what, my first thought was, a dancing partner? Then I remembered how I'd slept in the hospital with my teddy bear nestled by my side. I had found real comfort in that little stuffed animal.

She, too, sent me home with a tape. I drank the bitter, musty Ginseng tea she offered—"gives you energy and boosts your immune system"—but I refused her offer of homeopathic potions, the so-called Bach flower remedies.

As I left, almost fled, from her apartment, I wondered what in the world I was doing there. Was I going to turn into one of these muddle-headed alternative junkies, fumbling my crystals like rosary beads and consulting my astrologer before I made any decision? Was I going to end up at some Mexican clinic, being treated with laetrile and coffee enemas?

My oncologist's nurse, a small, soft-spoken Hispanic woman with an endless supply of compassion, had downplayed the side effects of my first treatment. No, I wouldn't need anyone to come with me to the office, unless I felt anxious. If I did get very nauseated and begin to vomit, it certainly wouldn't happen until some hours afterward. Her cheerful lack of concern went a long way toward allaying my fears.

I decided that I didn't want anyone to come to the doctor's office with me, that I would feel stronger on my own, putting up the brave front that was quickly becoming second nature. Besides, after all the interruptions of the past three weeks, Tom needed to get back to work. By the time I became really ill, if indeed I did, he would be home to take care of me.

After all the anxiety and preparation leading up to it, my first chemotherapy treatment was anti-climactic. As I sat on the examining table, the nurse expertly found a vein, inserted a small "butterfly" needle attached to a tube, and then made quick work of injecting the contents of the two large syringes, and one smaller one, telling me what each one was before injecting it. Methotrexate, fluorouracil, Decadron—another cortisone used for its anti-emetic properties. I felt nothing, except for a slight metallic taste in my mouth, and an odd tingle, like a small electric shock, in my genitals—which she assured me was typical and would quickly pass. Asking me to turn around, she gave me a shot of Compazine in my hip, for nausea. That stung, but the rest had been quite painless.

The whole thing took perhaps five minutes. I didn't even have time to visualize my imaginary "friend." The nurse placed a Band-Aid over the small puncture wound on the inside of my arm, and smiled at me.

"Okay," she said. "You're done for today."

"You mean that's it?" I asked incredulously, looking at the Band-Aid on my arm, which was decorated with Mickey and Minnie Mouse. "That's all there is to it?"

She nodded. "Call if you have any problems, but I really don't think you will. I think you'll do fine."

"Should I go home and rest?"

She shook her head. "Get out and do something. It'll take your mind off how you feel."

It was a beautiful day, and I decided to walk home around the Central Park reservoir. My spirits were high that day. Piece of cake, I thought, as I strolled down Broadway, looking at the shops. I can do this.

Over the course of the afternoon, I waited to develop symptoms. By dinnertime, I had a slight backache and felt vaguely out of sorts. Tom brought home some chicken soup from a Polish restaurant near his office.

"I'm afraid to eat," I told him, but I finished the whole bowl.

By the time I went to bed that night, I had decided that chemotherapy wasn't going to be all that bad. Maybe the relaxation tapes or the hypnotic suggestions made by the exotic lady had worked, after all. Maybe my bear friend Willy was hovering over me somewhere, like a guardian angel. Or perhaps the women I'd spoken with on the phone were right, and chemotherapy just wasn't the horror-show it was cracked up to be. Whatever it was, I didn't feel all that terrible—a little achy and flu-like, a touch of nausea, nothing more.

The next week when I went in for my treatment, I asked the oncologist if he thought I could manage a trip to California at the end of my fourth week of treatment. "Is it important to you?" he asked.

Two groups of art lovers, museum patrons and collectors—one in San Francisco and one in Los Angeles—had gotten together to pool expenses and bring me out to give readings from my book. Flattered by their interest, I had already accepted their invitation before my diagnosis, and had been looking forward to the trip. It was the kind of thing an author is supposed to do, and I wanted to do it.

"I guess I'd better let them know I can't come," I had told Tom at some point during that crazy week before my surgery.

"Maybe you should go anyway," he said. "I think it would be good for you."

"Oh, I couldn't."

"I would come with you."

My eyes filled with tears. "You would do that, for me?"

"Of course I would," he said. "Look, just tell them the situation, that you still want to come but can't promise anything, and see if they're flexible."

My call, of course, had met with a very sympathetic response, and I still hoped to go.

"Yes, it's important," I told the oncologist.

"It will mean delaying the next treatment two days. You'll have to see my associate."

"Is that really going to make a big difference?"

"Well, no, I guess we can work around it."

"So I can go?"

Although he was only a few years older than I, he looked at me sternly, as if he were a father admonishing his teenaged daughter not to go out with a questionable young man. "Chances are, you'll have more symptoms then than you do now, you know."

In that, the oncologist was perfectly correct. By the time I left for California I was no longer breezing through my weekly injections. I had begun to lose some hair, and I was worried about my appearance. After my shower each day, I'd find a nest of hair in the drain. My towels and clothes were covered with loose strands. In the shop where I bought the falsies I put in my bra to appear balanced, I found a little cloche cap, with a lock of hair in the front. This I would carry with me in case I woke up one morning and found all my hair still on my pillow or in a wet, tangled mass clogging the bathtub drain. Although my oncologist's nurse kept telling me this wouldn't happen with oral Cytoxan, I had read about it happening to other women, and I was taking no chances.

I hated the Cytoxan pills, with their poisonous blue crystals. Between the effects of those and the gastric irritation caused by the prednisone tablets, my whole digestive tract felt raw. The foul smell of incomplete digestion hovered around me. I was chewing Mylanta tablets a dozen times a day, and I had mouth sores—large white, painful patches on the inside of my cheeks and soft palate. I developed a taste for soft, cold foods, like pudding and ice cream.

When Tom and I climbed on the plane bound for Los Angeles six weeks after my surgery, I had just received my third course of chemotherapy. As luck would have it, the plane was half empty, and we found two rows of unoccupied center seats and stretched out. Tom was instantly asleep, as usual. I lay there with my headphones, listening to the soothing voice of the California psychologist, telling me to relax, let go, and let the shower of golden light wash over me. The batteries were running down, and the voice on the tape became slower and slower until finally it ground to a basso profundo halt. I sat up, miserable, and tried to watch the movie. My stomach was churning; my skin was crawling. I wanted to be at home, in my own bed. Why was I making this trip? What was I trying to prove?

At the airport in Los Angeles, we rented a car and drove up the coast to Ventura, where I could recuperate before giving my talk, and spend time with our friends Michael and Kay, who had just had a baby six weeks before.

Driving there, I was remembering the evening of the day after my biopsy, when we had called all our friends. The most poignant call had been to Kay. At forty-two, she was pregnant with her first child, whose arrival was eagerly anticipated any day.

"I'm in labor!" she had cried exultantly, before I had a chance to say anything. "But how did you know? You must be psychic!"

It was instantly clear that the last thing Kay needed at that moment was to hear about my problems. She needed every ounce of her energy and concentration for her labor and delivery. I back-pedaled furiously, murmuring something about intuition and how close we must still be, despite the 3,000 miles separating us.

"How do you feel?" I asked.

"Excited. Scared. Listen, I have to get ready. Michael will call you as soon as we know anything," she promised.

"I'm so happy for you," I said, hoping my voice conveyed that. For a moment I forgot myself, excited that at last she was about to have the child she had always wanted so much.

Kay and I had become friends in a women's group during the early 1970s, at a time when sisterhood meant more than almost anything else. Though we had each moved away from Ohio, she westward and I eastward, we had kept in touch, and we often arranged to spend part of a vacation together to renew our friendship.

That evening, the baby cried his way through our dinner in a nearby restaurant. When we got back to their house and he was at last asleep, the four of us sat and watched a videotape of the labor and birth, complete with titles and musical soundtrack. A California ritual, evidently, acceptable even when there is a Caesarean birth.

Later that night, while the men talked in the living room, Kay and I sat together in peaceful silence in the bedroom while she nursed little Benjamin. I remember looking at her full breasts, at the sweet, small face suckling contentedly against them.

As if to fill the ache located there, I covered the place where my own right breast had been with my hand, and felt the foam pad in the surgical bra that preserved the outer illusion of my wholeness. Those early months, I often found myself hunched over giving the "mastectomy salute," as I've heard this involuntary protective gesture called. This slumping caused terrific cramps in my shoulders. I was constantly having to remind myself to sit up straight, throw out what was left of my chest, and relax my arms.

Most of my woman friends were a few years younger than I, and had delayed having children until their late thirties—or, in the case of Kay, even later. By the time the women's movement caught up with me, the die had already been cast. I was a child of the fifties: early marriage, immediate children.

My own childbearing years, now twenty-five years behind me, felt like part of another lifetime. My babies were grown men now, but I could still remember so vividly what it had been like, how they had felt in my arms, as I looked at my friend Kay, a *madonna con bambino* with her dark curly hair and olive skin. She radiated a glow of contentment and satisfaction.

By then, although it hadn't happened yet, I realized that the chemotherapy would put me into menopause, on the other side of that threshold from my friends.

Many women aren't told in advance that chemotherapy will shut down their ovaries, at least temporarily, and often permanently, if they are over forty. The brochure given me by my oncologist made just one small reference to "cessation of menstruation," and didn't even mention hot flashes or menopause.

My sadness that night was tinged with bitterness. I'd been too young when my children were born, and too set-upon by circumstances, to fully savor moments like these. All the regrets I had about my sons' early years, and that first, impossible marriage to their father, washed over me.

If only, I thought, if only I could do it all over, the right way, with more love and patience and a good partner. How different it would be.

At last, Kay put the sleeping baby down and turned to me, her face sober.

"Do you feel like talking about it?" she asked.

I told her everything, as the baby slept on the bed between us, telling the whole long narrative of diagnosis, surgery, chemotherapy, all in that same, flat matter-of-fact way I had perfected those last weeks. My exhilarating sense of mission, of purpose, was nowhere to be found that evening, but at least I managed not to cry.

Not, that is, until Kay asked to see my scar, and then showed me hers, from the C-section.

We both wept together then, for our changed lives, for the terrible irony of the conjunction of these two momentous events—her birth, my mastectomy. Each had left scars, but one represented new life, and the other, the threat of death. Each was a part, I remember thinking, of some great cycle of female energy.

I couldn't help but compare my life with hers in the inevitable way one always does with close friends of the same sex. But I couldn't make sense of it—her gain, my loss. There was no sense to be made.

The world, the whole damn world, was upside down.

FIVE

Bearing Witness

What I really want to know is how to live with illness.
The help I want is not a matter of answering questions
but of witnessing attempts to live in certain ways.

I do not want my questions answered; I want my
experiences shared.

— ARTHUR FRANKS,
At the Will of the Body

MY PECULIAR STATE of elation persisted during the entire six weeks I was taking prednisone. While there were low moments, most of the time I existed in a chemically induced state of grace. The writer Max Lerner, under treatment for prostate cancer and lymphoma, accurately described the effects of this drug—which saw him through what he described as "some of my dreariest days"—as having induced a "compulsive euphoria." It was true. I felt energized, high on life, sleeping four or five hours a night, if that, and spending hours on the phone with my California friends, who would still be awake when everyone in New York had gone to sleep.

Tom would come home from work and ask me how I was feeling, a look of concern on his face. I would be waiting for him, high as a kite, bursting with insights and excitement. It became almost laughable, this incongruous giddiness, a joke between us. "Well," Tom would say, shaking his head. "I guess you ought to enjoy it while you've got it."

Not everyone feels this good on prednisone, however. A powerful corticosteroid, its common side effects include fluid retention, mood changes, and increased appetite, even with short-term use.

With the weekly injections, my blood counts had begun to plummet. My heartburn and stomach irritation had been resolved by taking Zan-

tac, an ulcer drug that suppressed acid production. Since my hair had begun to come out in alarming handfuls, I decided to buy a wig while I
still had enough hair to match it with.

In the small private cubicle at the wig salon, the chatty attendant
fussed over me, giving the elastic netting a firm tug behind the ears before
pinning it just so, teasing the synthetic curls, holding the mirror for me
to admire, then calling in other attendants for obligatory raves.

I felt as I often have in beauty parlors and at make-up counters—
estranged from myself. I was not raised to primp and powder. When I
participate in these female rituals, I often feel as if I am part of a charade.
This person in the mirror is not me, but someone else's version of me.
As soon as I can, I will wash out the elaborately-teased set, scrub off all
the makeup.

It was the same with the wig. There was nothing wrong with the thing
itself; it was a perfectly nice one, matching my own hair remarkably well
in color and style. I realized that many women were appreciative of the
opportunity to look like themselves while in treatment.

But I knew when I walked out the door that I didn't want to wear my
wig. In fact, I never did wear it, even though I developed a pronounced
bald spot, and the third or so of my hair that remained became brittle
and my scalp sore and red, as if sunburnt. I gained new empathy for my
husband's baldness. "And mine's not going to grow back, either!" he
reminded me.

Several times, I pinned the wig on and combed it as best I could, with
the pink plastic metal-toothed brush they had given me at the wig salon.
But I couldn't bring myself to go out in public with it on. It sat unused
on a white styrofoam head, waiting, where it still sits, in fact, on the top
shelf of my closet.

"Look on the bright side," said my oncologist's nurse. "The fact that
you're losing your hair means the chemo's working." Before every treatment, she brought me an ice-cap of frozen gel that fitted tightly over my
head. I wore this during and after my injections, in the hope that the cold
would impair the circulation to my scalp and spare the hair follicles the
full toxic effect of the chemicals. I sat there shivering, glad at least that
it was summer and warm outside.

I was still reading voraciously, deep in the throes of researching my
affliction. A person looking at my library shelves could tell a great deal

about my life's traumas from the clusters of books that appear there. Divorce, depression, weight loss—and now cancer. At every difficult juncture of my life, I have calmed and expanded myself by reading.

For me, increased knowledge yields a sense of intellectual mastery that always lends a certain perspective to the pain, especially when the situation itself cannot be resolved. Although I may have no more actual control than before, I feel as if I do, simply because I understand—or think that I do. It's a persuasive incentive for learning.

Some people can shut out anxiety by closing their eyes and ears. I am the opposite: I feel compelled to take it all in, an illustration of what psychiatrist E. Fuller Torrey once termed "the Rumpelstiltskin Principle." If something can be named and described, it is thereby transformed.

After my cancer was first diagnosed, what I hungered for above all else was an echo for what I'd seen and felt, and a sense of what to expect in the future. I had read all I could take of pamphlets, journal articles, and medical texts. The earnest, useful volumes on coping with the emotional aspects of illness had been helpful too, packed as they were with information about finding resources, making choices, seeking out support.

But I wanted more. I wanted stories. I hungered to read about the particular doubts, the fears, the isolation, the small satisfactions, the frustrations and triumphs—in short, the entire inner life of the woman living through a breast cancer diagnosis, its treatment, and the aftermath.

Those memoirs that I found, I eagerly devoured, and I was left each time with an appetite for more. Some were written by celebrities, commanding their readership by providing glimpses into the troubled lives of people we ordinarily envy and idealize. Others were inspirational in nature, straightforward tales of heroism in which the cancer patient was sustained by her faith in God and her family's love.

In my search, I also discovered a number of books and pamphlets, of the kind sold in health food stores, by people outside (and opposed to) the traditional medical structure, who claimed to have healed themselves or others by unorthodox nutritional strategies, like macrobiotics; new herbal or chemical treatments, such as hydrogen peroxide or ginseng; or homeopathy.

A close cousin to these were the many books on self-healing, with their anecdotes of terminally-ill patients now cancer-free through the curative powers of faith, love and positive thinking, often in combination with various other pop-psychology remedies. While I was curious about their methods, I could feel myself bristling at the slightest suggestion that I had "participated" in my illness. At best, these books seemed to offer the reader coping strategies and a feeling of personal empowerment. But at worst, they ran the risk of adding guilt to the burden the ill person must bear, by forcing an examination of causes or creating an unrealistic expectation of cure.

Reluctantly, I abandoned my search. With few exceptions, I decided that when it came to reading about illness, what people seemed most intrigued by was only a small step beyond what the supermarket tabloids had for sale: sensational crises, freaks, medical breakthroughs, cures, and noble deaths—especially of children. These less-than-common experiences were easy to swallow; they could be readily imbued with high drama, heart-rending emotionality, and feel-good spiritual inferences.

But real life is rarely like that.

What these stereotyped stories make us lose touch with, it seems to me, is the mundane, day-to-day feel of what it's like to encounter the darker aspects of our human heritage—to live with disability, with chronic illness, with despair and uncertainty, with the threat of impending loss of function and death.

An editor friend passed on a copy of a book that provided a gritty taste of exactly what I was looking for, a collection of women's personal experiences with breast cancer, candid and unvarnished. The book, still in manuscript at the time, was later published as *Women Talk About Breast Surgery*. I consumed it in an afternoon, marveling at the diversity of choices and treatments and emotions. While I didn't identify with every woman in the book, I did find my own reactions mirrored in many of these womens' perceptions.

My sole frustration was that I couldn't talk back to these women, to raise issues the authors hadn't thought to ask, or to tell them my story and compare experiences.

I was no longer in contact with the six women I had spoken with by telephone during the week or so after my diagnosis. It didn't seem right, taking more of the time they had so generously offered in the midst of my crisis. Besides, what I needed was not more information.

I needed to know that I was not isolated with my predicament. If I was to let go of my need for certainty, and accept the imponderables of my diagnosis, I wanted the consolation of companionship in return. I wanted my experience witnessed, and I wanted to witness the experience of others.

At the end of six weeks of intensive chemotherapy, I stopped taking the prednisone. My oncologist gave me a three-week reprieve for my blood counts to recover before the next bi-weekly series began. Two of those weeks I spent in Amagansett, Long Island, on the beach, with Tom joining me for weekends. I read, listened to my tapes, shopped for fruits and vegetables at the farmer's market, and prepared healthy feasts. I couldn't sunbathe because of the sun sensitivity caused by the Methotrexate, but I went for long walks on the beach, strolling barefoot in the surf, feeling stronger and less nauseated with every passing day.

Back at home in the city, my buoyant good spirits departed for good. I began my next cycle of treatments, and almost immediately I sank into a deep depression. While I still spoke with my friends, and they called to inquire how I was—though less frequently, as time went on—I found myself becoming more and more distant from them. My troubles outweighed theirs, I felt. I envied them their unblemished lives, their unscarred bodies, their certain futures. They could not, I felt sure, understand.

Besides, I had nothing new to report. How many times can you talk about nausea and hair loss without turning into a complete bore? The chemo had become predictable, unpleasant and fatiguing, but routine. Yet I longed for attention, particularly from my women friends, some reaching-out on their part that would fill the hollow place inside.

But I was "handling it so well"—or so everyone said. Though I was miserable enough, I certainly wasn't experiencing the horrendous side effects my friends had heard about.

Being a model patient is a variation on an old theme for me. As a child, I had always managed my loneliness by being a teacher's pet, wrapping my fragile, isolated self in the cotton batting of adult approval.

Almost forty years later, nothing had changed. A month after my mastectomy, refusing the help of friends, there I was, breezing alone into my oncologist's office for my weekly injections, making pleasant conversation with his nurses. While they probed to find new veins, we would talk about their families and vacations. You would never have guessed that my chest was still healing, or that I was getting toxic chemicals pumped into my body, with plummeting blood counts, mouth sores, ulcers and all the other accompanying miseries.

A self I'd been struggling for years to overthrow rose up again victorious, in all her uncomplaining, self-righteous virtue, eager to throw herself under the wheels. I was still that same obedient child. The good little girl—no, more than good. Heroic. The perfect cancer personality profile, as some researchers would maintain. Nice, sweet, the doormat. Slow to anger and quick to put the needs of others before her own.

See you next week, I'd say, and smile. Then I would go home, cry, and wait for the sickness to begin.

As the attention of my friends and family waned, the full magnitude of what had happened began to sink in. The best I could manage, from then on, was stoic endurance. The worst was the blind irrational anger I felt at the monstrous unfairness of it all, a black fury that could be drawn like lightning to any unsuspecting target—a lab technician, trying to draw blood from a collapsed vein; my therapist, for his insufficient grasp of what I was going through; the oncologist, at a conference in the Far East (How dare he leave me to his associate, whom I barely knew!); my husband for being too busy, or too tired, to listen to my complaints.

At first, the summer heat masked my hot flashes. After a few weeks, however, they became unmistakable. Tom slept under blankets, while I turned on the air conditioner full blast and slept naked beside him. Even so, I awakened bathed in sweat five or six times a night. A dozen or more times a day, a wave of intense heat would leave me drenched and red-faced, my heart pounding.

"I think I'm going through menopause," I told my oncologist.

He reminded me that ovarian cells are among the many rapidly dividing cells in the body affected by chemotherapy. Because of my age, it wasn't likely that my hormone level would recover, even after treatment, he said. I asked him for a referral to a new gynecologist.

"I'm having hot flashes," I told the gynecologist, after he had examined me.

"Yes," he said. "I imagine you are."

"They're really awful, in this heat. Isn't there something you can do?"

He shook his head and reiterated what I already knew, that women with breast cancer should not receive hormone replacement therapy in any form, even if their tumors were ER-negative, as mine was. In fact, before the advent of tamoxifen, a widely used drug which is an estrogen antagonist, women whose tumors were ER-positive often had their ovaries removed as part of treatment.

Even though I was ER-negative, estrogen was not considered safe for me. It was just going to have to be fans and short sleeves, even in the dead of winter—and vaginal lubricants, for the rare times I was in the mood for sex.

"If you find anything that helps," the gynecologist said as I left his office, "let me know."

True to form, I bought a book or two on menopause and investigated a few natural remedies. I began using Vitamin E cream and taking evening primrose oil, but to no avail.

In the wake of my elation, and with these new, disturbing symptoms, I felt even more helpless. All my life, without even realizing it, I'd retained an innocent trust in my physical being. Now, that was lost, replaced by the feeling of having been betrayed by the runaway cells of my own body.

I felt alone with my illness. No one I knew, with the exception of Tom, understood what I was going through. But he was in the middle of a job change, and needed to devote his energies full-time to his career. Though he was careful not to say anything, it was clear that work had become a refuge for him, an escape from the graveness of my situation. Tom was finding himself doing altogether too much caretaking. Most of us can set aside our own needs in an emergency, but when that crisis goes on and on, it becomes another story.

With chemotherapy—and, often, without it—the entire experience of dealing with breast cancer extends beyond crisis and turns into a siege, a long, distressing and enervating process—and this is presupposing there is no recurrence of the cancer. The months pass, the physical wounds heal. Goodwill and resources have long ago been consumed, yet the need for reassurance and support persists. The fears, if anything, intensify.

Long before I was ready to do so, the people in my life were eager for me to "get on with it." "Put it behind you," I was urged by well-meaning friends. "Get back to your writing. That's the best thing you can do." Yet, when I sat down to write, I found myself divided, distracted. It was far too soon to write about the cancer, yet my illness was so much at the center of my universe, I couldn't focus with any clarity on anything else.

Pressed for time, my doctors, while sympathetic, could be of little help. In my reading, I had found only models of women whose brave optimism and fighting spirit had brought them "victory" and the admiration of others—or, conversely and much more distressing, women whose courage had stood fast through lingering, valiant deaths. I was not inspired by this. Compared with them, I could only find fault with myself.

Progressively worn down by the chemotherapy, mutilated by the surgery, anxiety-ridden over the future, I felt neither brave nor optimistic. As for fighting spirit, it was all I could do to follow my daily routine. At times, I felt angry enough to fight, perhaps; but I lacked an enemy, a target.

Never had I felt so anxious. Even with the constant nausea, I was overeating again. I felt out of control, putting food in my mouth when I wasn't hungry, stuffing my feelings down and putting back all the weight I had lost, and more. I began to wonder what was wrong with me. The fundamental sense of stability that had always stood like a firm platform beneath my feet was eroding away, bit by bit.

I found myself easily knocked off balance, often by small things that would never have bothered me before. I was acutely sensitive to slights by others. Even with the exhaustion produced by the chemotherapy, I had difficulty sleeping. More and more, I found myself trying on the familiar labels that women characteristically pin on themselves—dependent, depressed, hysterical.

I complained too much. I knew that, but I couldn't seem to stop myself. In Tom's silences, I imagined rebukes. I kept hearing his voice saying: pull yourself together, stop malingering, stop feeling sorry for yourself. This has gone on long enough.

I could only agree. I, too, was sick and tired of being sick and tired. Yet, the siege persisted.

But where to turn for consolation? Soon after my diagnosis, I discovered how alarming my story was to others. I would meet someone I hadn't seen for a while, tell them my news, and watch them move from shock into speechlessness, then awkwardly try to change the subject. Clearly, it was anger that moved me to do this. Why should they get off easy, when I was so miserable?

Finally, because I sensed that no one really wanted to witness my experience, I stopped talking about it. Friends would ask how I was, but they didn't really want to know. Or so I thought. In retrospect, I'm not so sure. Perhaps they, sensing my anger and not wishing to draw fire, were merely giving me a wide berth, awaiting a time when I might be more receptive. Perhaps they simply didn't know what to say.

I couldn't blame my friends for pulling away. I considered times when I had done the same, when one or another friend had become seriously ill and I had let my own feelings of powerlessness and fear drive a wedge between us. I knew what it was not to know how to help. I, too, had fled from hospital rooms after fifteen tense minutes of inanities. There are times that no one knows what to do, or say. That is, after all, the essence of helplessness.

I hadn't known then—as I did so clearly now that it was I who was ill—that there is always something a friend can do. A friend can simply be there. A friend can bear witness.

Trying to offer reassurance is rarely helpful, yet this is what our anxiety provokes us to do when confronted with a serious and perhaps irresolvable problem. In the name of love, we serve up the most inane pieties. I'm sure you'll be fine, we say. It'll all work out for the best. You'll feel better soon. The gravely ill person often feels pushed away by statements such as these. What begins as reassurance becomes estrangement.

Advice giving can be even worse, insulting the intelligence of the ill person, who usually knows perfectly well "what to do." Invariably, such advice is rebuffed. If the advice giver is persistent, however, a frustrating round robin of "Why don't you?" and "Yes, but . . . " interactions is bound to ensue.

Specious comparisons can be equally offensive. In her eagerness to sympathize and identify, a friend may compare a minor ailment or problem of her own with the predicament of her friend's breast cancer. Offered in the spirit of commonality, such a comparison can seem to diminish the gravity of the cancer patient's situation, and lead to further feelings of isolation.

The need to contain or control the ill person's experience, rather than to tolerate and simply acknowledge the grief, anger and fear of what has happened, is what drives well-meaning friends and family members to offer advice, reassurance, or faulty comparisons from their own lives.

What I call bearing witness is altogether different. Without realizing it, it was this that I longed for. Bearing witness involves a mutual recognition of helplessness, vulnerability and respect. It says only, I am with you. I honor your experience. How simple, yet how rare a gift this is.

My appointment book for that summer was filled with escapes—the time in Amagansett, a long weekend on the Jersey shore, a trip to Ireland with Tom for the opening of an exhibition of my father's drawings in Dublin. At the end of August, we planned a two-week holiday at the house on Cape Cod that we had been renting for thirteen summers with our oldest and dearest friends. All summer long, with my growing feelings of isolation, I had looked forward to this time, imagining that in the company of these friends, this aching separateness I felt would drop away.

I was particularly looking forward to having the time for long, intimate talks with my friend Bob, who had been HIV-positive and under treatment with AZT for some time. I envisaged long walks on the beach, deep in conversation, sharing our experiences. Our fears, and the rigors of treatment, I thought, would give us a common bond, even though the life-threatening diseases we were confronting were very different.

When I got there, it soon became clear that Bob didn't want to talk or think about his illness. This was supposed to be a vacation, after all. I felt—was this only my imagination?—a certain coolness from him, as if my cancer or the way I was dealing with it were an affront to him, in some way. At that stage, denial and stoicism were still serving him well. If anything, far from engendering support and communality, my own obvious emotionality only drew his disdain.

Kay and Michael had come from California with their baby, and another couple from Cambridge were there, with their two-year-old son. At another point in time, I would not have minded a child-centered vacation. These were my oldest friends, after all; had I felt less childlike myself, I might have shared in the pleasures of parenting. As it was, I was miserable. The effects of the chemotherapy had altered my tolerance for anything disruptive. After the first few hours, the normal crying and noise of young children became hard to take.

I felt rather like a jealous, displaced sibling myself, pushed to the side by these new arrivals. I envied the children for the way they could command attention so easily. *I* needed too, but as an adult, I couldn't cry or whine about it.

Aside from Tom, there was one other person there at the house on Cape Cod with whom I felt at ease. Fran and I had first grown close a dozen years before, when her husband Steven was dying from brain cancer. She seemed to know, from her own experience, what it was that I needed. All the time we were there, Fran kept reaching out to me, asking me how I was doing, hugging me, making small solicitous gestures.

Looking back, I can see that my mistrust of others was most evident with my therapist. At the time, I didn't see it that way, of course. The rift between us seemed real, and unbridgeable. As a healthy man in the prime of life, he couldn't possibly comprehend what it felt like to lose a breast or to live with the fear of recurrence, as I did. Besides, his caring was purchased. He was just a hired friend, one who didn't—couldn't—understand.

I didn't see what later became evident, that I was pushing all of them away—my friends, my therapist, even Tom—that while they were at a loss sometimes with me, it was really I who resented and envied their health and good fortune. I was not fun to be with. I was fast becoming the joyless embodiment of that old saw, "misery loves company."

Back in the city from Cape Cod, it finally occurred to me that misery *could* have company, if she wanted. I pulled out the sheet of resources the hospital social worker had given me, and called a name at the cancer rehabilitation center attached to the hospital where I'd had my surgery, to inquire about a support group for breast cancer patients.

Led by a social worker who carefully screened the participants and kept the discussion focused, the group met every week in a drab conference room behind a snack bar. Of the eight women there, I was one of the oldest. This was a surprise. I hadn't realized how many women in their thirties and early forties were being diagnosed with breast cancer. As I later discovered, younger, premenopausal women form a substantial and a growing minority of cases.

At the first meeting, I sat and listened, overcome with relief and a growing satisfaction at the free-wheeling open discussion of so many of the issues that were on my mind, too: depression and anger at the mutilation of surgery, the rigors of chemotherapy, and at the just plain unfairness of having cancer; fears of recurrence and death; feelings of estrangement from family and friends. In the course of an hour-and-a-half meeting, the group touched on all these things, and compared notes on more practical problems that group members had encountered. There was much talk about the best ways of dealing with doctors and the medical community, of managing the side effects of chemotherapy, of the pros and cons of reconstructive surgery, and of the symptoms of menopause. As each woman spoke, heads would nod, and others would offer up their own related experiences.

When it was my turn, I told them how depressed I had been feeling, that the chemo seemed endless, that I felt lonely and uncared about by my friends. I told them I'd had no one to talk with except for Tom, and that I was worried about the strain on our relationship. I told them I hadn't been able to write for months, that my memory and concentration were lousy.

"They tell you that chemotherapy doesn't alter your mood or your thinking," Penny said. "But that's nonsense."

The most verbal member of the group, Penny was a small, smartly dressed woman in her early forties, with dark eyes and a ready smile; it had been two years since her mastectomy. "Maybe it's the exhaustion," she continued, "or the lack of hormones, or just plain depression. Whatever it is, it changes you. They don't like to admit that, but it's true."

"I was in a complete fog during my chemo," Ronnie said. "Especially toward the end."

Ronnie was a serious, intense woman in her late thirties, with dark curly hair and round glasses. She had elected to have a lumpectomy with radiation.

"I didn't realize how bad it was until after it was over," Miriam offered. "When I started to feel better. It was like peeling off another dirty overcoat every day."

Miriam, approaching fifty, wore no makeup and jeans. She had cropped straight hair and was somewhat overweight. Her cancer had spread to the lymph nodes, I remembered from the earlier discussion.

"How long did it take before you felt like yourself again?" I asked.

"A month or two, at least."

"For me, it was more like six months," Ronnie interjected.

"I still don't feel like my old self, and it's been a year and a half since

I was diagnosed," Pat chimed in. "They said I would probably get my periods back, but I never did."

Pat, a tall, slender woman in her early thirties with very short hair, was unmarried and childless. Her cancer, too, had spread to the lymph nodes.

There was a somber silence for a moment.

"Well, I think you're doing pretty well, considering you're right in the middle of your treatment," said Penny, turning back to me. "Why don't you give yourself some credit for getting through this as well as you are?"

"I don't think I'm doing all that well," I said.

"What do you expect? Miracles? I mean, be realistic: you're dealing with mortality, disfigurement, menopause, constant uncertainty about the future. Naturally, you feel rotten. From what I can tell, you're doing just great."

"What other choice do I have?" I asked, somewhat mollified. "I can't just lie in bed feeling sorry for myself."

"Some people do. They just shut down completely, isolate themselves, give up."

"That's not me."

"Exactly. The very fact that you're here means you're a fighter."

"Well, maybe." I looked around at the other women in the group. "But the real reason I came was loneliness."

"I think we all felt isolated, before joining the group," Ronnie said.

Heads nodded. A chorus of agreements sounded.

Pat related a story about a woman friend who had complained to her at length about minor gynecological surgery. "I never really talked to her about my mastectomy, and here she was, comparing herself with me, making a big deal out of this trivial procedure. I should have been sympathetic, I guess, but all I felt was resentful. Maybe it was wrong of me, but I just couldn't respond to her."

"You wanted her to be stoic, like you were," said Penny.

"Yeah." Pat laughed. "Maybe more so. She had less right to complain, after all."

"What about turning it around, then, and talking to her?"

Pat looked incredulous. "No way! She didn't want to hear about me."

"How can you be so sure? Did you ever ask her?"

"No, I just knew. My getting breast cancer scared the shit out of most of my friends. I mean, it's every woman's worst fear, right? When I'd try to tell them what it was like, they'd get this worried look on their faces, and start obsessing about the lumps in their breasts. I couldn't talk to them."

"Friends mean well, but they just don't understand," Rosa said. "Not unless it's happened to them."

Rosa, who had been silent until then, had been listening intently to the discussion. A young mother of a three-year-old boy, she was dark-haired and soft-spoken.

"It's true," Miriam said. "Even my husband, who's been just terrific through all of this, very supportive, gets to the point where he can't listen to it anymore. I don't blame him. I mean, it's depressing."

"That's where the group comes in. Having a place to talk about it helps your other relationships, don't you think?" commented Penny. "I don't even try to talk with other people about having cancer anymore. I just don't feel like I need to."

"I'd have a hard time accepting that," said Ronnie. "For myself, I mean. What's the point of having friends, if you can't be close to them?"

"The thing is, everyone just expects you to get on with your life," Pat said. "After the first month or two, even your friends don't want to hear your problems anymore. They get sick and tired of it."

"So do I," said Miriam.

"Yeah, that's right," Rosa said. "I get so angry when my sisters come over. All they want to do is talk about their husbands and kids, like everything's the same as it was. I feel like tearing my blouse off and screaming at them."

"What would you scream?" asked Penny.

Two tears spilled down Rosa's cheeks. " 'Look what happened to me! Don't you care?' That's what I feel like saying."

"So why don't you?"

"They'd think I was crazy."

"Maybe they're just scared of saying the wrong thing. Have you considered that?"

"Well, no." Rosa wiped her eyes. "I miss them a lot. We used to tell each other everything. Maybe I will try to talk to them."

There was a companionable silence. I put my hand up to touch the spot at the crown of my head where my hair was thinnest. "Can I change the subject?" I asked.

There was a general nodding of assent.

"I bought this expensive wig, but I haven't worn it yet," I said. "It just doesn't feel like me."

"Your own hair looks all right to me," Penny said.

"But it's so brittle and dry. See this?" I showed them my bald spot, and brushed off the several strands of hair that had come off in my hand. "My hair was always my best feature. It's so weird, worrying about this—it's like it shouldn't matter, but it does. I was never vain before. I honestly didn't think that losing my hair would bother me so much."

"It's not vanity," Ronnie said. "You think it's trivial, but it's not. It's just the visible part of this whole thing. Everything else is hidden. Losing your hair is like announcing to the world: 'Look, I have cancer.' "

"I never could bring myself to wear my wig either," said Miriam to me. "And I had a whole lot less hair even than you."

"Weren't you self-conscious when you were out in public?" I asked.

"Yes, but the wig didn't make me feel any better. I got into scarves and hats a lot."

"Consider yourself lucky. I didn't have a choice." Pat's hair was obviously just growing in. Her very short, boyish haircut was quite becoming with her long neck and small, well-shaped head. "I was on Adriamycin, and so I lost all my hair, including my eyebrows and eyelashes, twice. Not to mention my pubic hair—God, I looked like a plucked chicken! I can't tell you how great it feels not to be wearing that hot, smelly thing on my head."

"Well, I don't mind my wig." Another woman, who was a few years older than the others and who had been silent until now, patted her shoulder-length salt-and-pepper curls. "In fact, everyone tells me it's very becoming."

That night I lay in bed, thinking about the group, trying to remember the women's names and savoring what each of them had said. For the first time in months, I felt validated. The loneliness was gone. There was so much to talk about. I couldn't wait for the next meeting.

It was a diverse group. During the year I attended these weekly gatherings, there were fourteen women, besides myself, in the meetings at one time or another. The sole organizing principle was that all of us had primary breast cancer and were eager to talk about it with other women in the same predicament. After that, all similarities ceased.

We represented the spectrum of breast cancer, in both diagnosis and prognosis. All but one of the major cancer centers in the metropolitan area were represented, with their differing treatment philosophies. Some of our cancers had been caught early. Others had been less fortunate, and the disease had already spread to the lymph nodes and, perhaps, beyond. We ranged in age from early thirties to late sixties, with the majority in their late thirties and forties.

Most of us had had mastectomies; of the two women with lumpectomies, one had a local recurrence after a year. Most of the women had been given six months of chemotherapy following diagnosis—some with CMF, as I had, and others, particularly those who had lymph node involvement, with Adriamycin as a part of the protocol. The drugs had been administered in differing ways, by infusion, injection, and indwelling catheter, and the dosage and number of cycles had varied as well.

For most of us who were young enough, chemotherapy had induced menopause, although some of the younger women had again begun to menstruate after treatment ended. Most of the women were also taking tamoxifen, in the hopes that hormone therapy would slow or stop the growth of any remaining cancer cells.

During the year I was in the group, two women besides myself had reconstructive surgery. One was well-satisfied with her new breast, the other unhappy with the results and concerned enough about the health risks of her implant that she planned on having it removed. The rest wore prostheses, except for one woman, who'd had bilateral mastectomies at different times, and who had decided that she was most comfortable going around flat-chested.

Some of the women entered the group as soon as they could after surgery. Others had waited months, or in some cases, years, until recurrent anxieties and loneliness had led them to seek help.

Several of us had gained weight during chemotherapy and struggled with taking off the excess pounds. Others seemed to have no problem with weight gain, though all of us tried, with varying degrees of success, to adhere to a low-fat diet.

A high-fat diet is one of the "lifestyle factors" that has been implicated in breast cancer causation, according to epidemiological studies of population groups and disease rates.

Our attitudes toward treatment had also been very different. Even after a local recurrence following her lumpectomy, one woman had insisted on a quadrantectomy, a wider excision that permitted her to keep most of her breast. Another had stopped her chemotherapy after the fourth month of treatment because of concern over her immune system functioning. Still others had sought out the most extensive surgery, and the most aggressive of chemotherapy treatments. For them, this was the route of least anxiety.

At first I found this degree of disparity among the group members disturbing. How could I ever be sure, I wondered, if what I had been given was the right treatment? If the choices I made were the right ones? The simple answer was, I couldn't. The women in the group taught me that, through the simple exercise of their diversity.

It was not an easy lesson to learn, but as I watched the others grappling with their choices, it became more and more clear that this business of having cancer, like so much else in life, was really in my hands. I would have to bear the consequences of my choices alone. But the privilege of witnessing the struggles of others made the journey seem far less daunting and lonely.

The group taught me to accept a new frame of reference as well. I had changed, but I hadn't wanted to accept it. Seeing other women coping with the changes having cancer had wrought in their lives, I stopped trying to recapture the energy and optimism of my pre-cancer self. Gradually, my expectations of myself began to change, to fit the emotional realities that now faced me.

The same fall that I joined this support group, Stanford psychiatrist David Spiegel published a groundbreaking study on the effects of group therapy with women with metastatic breast cancer, in the British medical journal *Lancet*.

The eighty-six women in his study, whose breast cancer had metastasized, were assigned randomly to group therapy plus conventional medical treatment, or to medical treatment alone, without therapy groups. The experimental and treatment groups were equivalent in every clinically used predictor of disease outcome. Led by a trained therapist, the therapy groups met weekly for a year, offering support and discussing their mutual concerns. Self-hypnosis for pain control was taught in the group as well. During the year, the women became close to one another, visiting each other in the hospital and attending members' funerals.

When Spiegel initiated the study thirteen years ago, his intent had been to disprove what he called "the wish-away-your-cancer types," he told interviewers. "The whole point of the original study was that we could make them feel better," he said. "We didn't in any way imply you were going to wish away your illness. In fact we were saying 'face your mortality.'" In fact, the patients who received therapy did become less anxious, fearful and depressed, as well as learning to better manage their pain.

Some years later, irritated with pop-psychology claims that positive thinking could conquer cancer, Spiegel decided to follow up on his study. "Here was a perfect setup," he remembers saying to himself. "I had shown this great psychological impact, and I knew there would be no difference in survival."

But there was. After an intervening period of about ten years, Spiegel was stunned to find a difference in longevity surpassing what anyone could have predicted: the women who had attended the groups lived, on average, *twice* as long (thirty-seven months) as those who had not (nineteen months). The three women still alive at the end of the study had all been in the therapy groups.

"I nearly fell off my chair," Spiegel said. "I just couldn't believe it."

He urged caution in interpreting his study, however. The results had not yet been replicated. Psychological and attitudinal change may not have affected the progression of disease. Better compliance with doctors' orders on medication and diet, or greater physical activity, are two alternative explanations for the differences between the two groups. "What I am flat out certain of is that something about being in the groups helped these women live longer," he said. "But what that is, I don't know."

Whatever that "something" was, I felt very fortunate to have my meetings.

Cancer seemed to be everywhere I looked that fall. Tom's older brother, Robert, a biochemist who lived in Columbus and taught at Ohio State University, was losing his two-year battle with esophageal cancer, a particularly deadly disease whose five-year survival rate is only eight percent. We had visited several times during his long illness, finding him weaker each time.

Despite his own failing health, Robert's support of me when I was first diagnosed had been warm and enthusiastic. His optimism and pragmatic approach had cheered me during low points in my chemotherapy. But finally, his body could withstand no more of the onslaught of toxic drugs that had been keeping the tumor at bay for eighteen months. Within two months, he had slipped into the terminal phase of his illness.

By early October, when Tom and I went out to Ohio to say our final good-byes, Robert was in a semi-comatose state. Too weak to speak or even open his eyes, he was still able to communicate by the faint squeezing of his right hand.

His wife Ina had told us to talk to him, that he could still understand, and so, when it was my turn, I bent over the hospital bed and spoke a few inadequate sentences about love and courage. I told him I was doing well, and thanked him for his help. For a long moment, he held my hand tightly.

After that weekend, the rest of the family went home, leaving his wife and children to their vigil. For almost two weeks after that, Robert managed to hang on. Then he was gone.

Meanwhile, cancer had entered my life from another quarter as well. Shortly after my surgery the previous May, my mother drew me aside one day in Woodstock.

"I think I've found something—you know, *there*," she said.

At eighty-one, motivated by what had happened to me, she had examined her breasts for the first time in her life and found a small lump. She guided my hand to the spot, and I could feel a pea-sized nodule under her tissue-thin skin.

I walked over to the telephone, knowing we were in for a battle. "Why don't I just call for an appointment right now?" I suggested.

"Oh, no," she said. "Absolutely not. I'm not going to have them doing to me what they did to you."

"But they wouldn't," I protested. "At your age, they'd probably just do a simple lumpectomy. They'd use local anesthesia. It's not much worse than having a tooth pulled."

"I don't care," she said. "I'm not going to let them touch me! I have far too many doctors as it is." She flung her hand in the direction of the bottles of medication lined up on the kitchen counter top. "Just look at all these pills I have to take! It's ridiculous!"

I begged, I pleaded, but to no avail.

"I should never have told you in the first place," she said.

"What are the chances it's not cancer?" I asked Donald when I got back to New York.

"Very remote, at her age," he replied.

"Can't you do something?" I asked her physician, when we spoke on the telephone the following week. "Can't you say something to her?"

He sighed. "Your mother has a mind of her own. I doubt that she'll listen to me, but I'll certainly give it a try."

Three months went by, during which time I would bring up the subject every week or two, only to have her angrily say no. It wasn't until October, after Robert's death, when I had only three more cycles of chemotherapy to go, that she agreed to see a surgeon.

Because of breathing problems, I had taken her to see a lung specialist, who urged her to see a surgeon and have the lump biopsied. Why she followed this doctor's advice, when she hadn't paid attention to her own internist or to me, was a complete mystery. Arrangements were made for the biopsy, bone and liver scans were done—all with my mother's reluctant cooperation.

Rather than being with her the day of her surgery as I had planned, I was at home in bed, in New York, with a bad case of the flu. I felt terrible. My nose was running. I was nauseated. I ached all over and felt feverish. But more than these physical symptoms, I felt done in emotionally.

My mother's biopsy confirmed that she, too, had breast cancer, although it was small and appeared to be localized. When I went in for my chemotherapy the following week, my flu was better, but I was still depressed. As soon as my oncologist entered the examining room, I burst into tears.

"What's wrong?" he asked. "You were doing so well."

"Everything," I said. "Everything's wrong."

A month later, the day after my final chemotherapy treatment, I sat down with the Mayer family at the Thanksgiving table. Across from me, Tom's father, Monroe—called Dad by everyone, including me—stood and raised his glass.

"Today, on this special occasion," he said, "I want us to remember those who are no longer with us." He mentioned Sandy, Donald's first wife, and "Mother," his affectionate name for his wife, Adrienne, who had borne him six children and who had died eight years earlier of lung cancer. At his son Robert's name, his voice trembled, and the tears stood in his eyes.

After a moment, he composed himself and went on. His eyes fell on me, seated opposite him, across the table. "And Musa," he said, almost as an afterthought. "We are glad she is with us, and hope only the best for her." Saluting me with his glass, he sipped his wine and sat down.

I lowered my eyes, stung by the unwitting cruelty of this toast. Dad hadn't meant to hurt me, of course. Surely I was just being oversensitive. But was that who I had become now—a provisional addendum to that short sad list of Mayers who had died of cancer?

Tom quickly raised his glass to toast the end of my chemotherapy. "Musa had her last treatment yesterday," he announced, squeezing my hand. "So we really do have something to be thankful for."

SIX

Looking for Answers

We are not to know why
this and that masters us;
real life makes no reply,
only that it enraptures us
makes us familiar with it.
— RAINER MARIA RILKE,
May 1924

POKING THROUGH THE fallen leaves of the previous autumn, silt-
ed down by winter into a brown membrane, was the milky,
trifoliate flower of a trillium. I knelt beside it.

It was a late spring day in Ohio, some thirteen years ago now, but I
can still recall vividly the pale blue of the sky, the new green leaves of
the poplars flashing in the light wind, the perfect flower that seemed to
have bloomed there for the occasion. Other people were also walking
slowly through the woods, alone and without speaking, as I was. Now
and then, I would catch glimpses of them through the dappled trunks
of the young sycamores. Some were weeping; the faces of others were
composed, meditative.

I let the last tablespoon or two of the ashes and bits of bone I had been
carrying in my hand sift through my fingers to the root of the trillium.

These were the last mortal remains of Joseph, dead at fifty-eight of
brain cancer. He had been my client at the mental health agency in Ohio
where I worked as a counselor. He had come to see me for a specific
reason, brandishing a new book called *Getting Well Again*, about healing
cancer through imagery and the emotions.

Joseph wanted help in learning to do the visualizations and other exercises suggested by the authors. A friend of his who had known of my

interest in mind-body issues and my experience with relaxation and guided imagery, had referred him to me.

A mathematician, a precise, gentle man with an unassuming manner, a sparse monk's tonsure of gray hair and wild, craggy eyebrows over mild, myopic blue eyes, Joseph wasted no time in telling me that he intended to refuse any further medical intervention. He was going to take charge of his illness himself, and fight the cancer if he could.

Explaining that I was no expert in these techniques, I taught him to relax and to envision the battle between his immune system and the cancer cells. Following the procedures outlined in the book, I helped him examine his life, his goals, his unfulfilled dreams. Together, we looked at his losses in recent years, at the so-called "benefits" of his illness. According to the author, Dr. O. Carl Simonton, getting sick might be functioning as a "permission giver." Cancer patients needed to discover other ways to get their needs met, if they were to be cured.

At first the sheer optimism of this enterprise energized Joseph. For such a modest and private man, this intense focus on himself was gratifying, if a bit alarming at first. "This stuff really works!" he'd report exultantly.

Then he began to lose ground. His pain came back. He lost his appetite. It became clear that he was rapidly getting worse. He would hobble up the walk on a cane, lower himself painfully into a chair. Finally, even that became too much. Telephone conversations took the place of face-to-face contact, and his talk turned more and more toward settling his affairs, finishing what was still left unfinished.

One day, I went to visit him at his little house on the edge of a bird sanctuary outside of town. Lying in a rented hospital bed beside sliding doors that opened to the fields and woods outside, and with a friend there to nurse him, Joseph seemed at peace.

I remember standing there at his bedside, shocked by how emaciated and pale he had become. "Sit down," he said, with a wan smile. "And don't look so worried."

After much deliberation, he said, he had decided to take his own life, rather than put himself and his friends through the pain and indignities of a long, drawn-out death. With the help of a compassionate physician, he had hoarded up enough medication to do the job. But it would have to be soon, while he still had the strength to take the pills himself.

I was invited to Joseph's farewell party, but I didn't go. That was a time for friends and family, I told him, and I was really neither. Later that day, he called me up, very tired, but obviously exalted. There had been music and flowers. Everyone had come. "I just want to rest now," he said. After we hung up, I wondered if that had been his way of saying good-bye. So be it, I thought.

But an hour later, Joseph was on the telephone again, in tears. "I've done it," he said. "I've actually done it."

"Do you want me to come over?"

"No, no," he said, "My friends are with me. I have what I need. I just wanted to say thank you for everything."

Gradually, he slipped into coma, where he lingered for a day or two. Following his wishes, his friends dressed the body, slipped it into the back of someone's station wagon, and took it to a crematorium. Like everything else about Joseph's death, this was strictly do-it-yourself. No undertaker, no coffin, no cemetery plot. "Joseph didn't want his money spent that way," a friend told me. "He thought it was a waste."

We stood in a large circle in a clearing outside his house, holding hands, telling anecdotes and tender stories about Joseph. One by one, we filed past the cardboard box with his name scrawled on it, each scooping out a handful of ashes, then wandering off into his beloved woods, to fertilize the bushes and trees and wildflowers there.

A few months later, I was approached by another cancer patient, this time a woman who had just had a mastectomy. Still disturbed by Joseph's death, I told her I didn't think I knew enough about the Simonton method to teach it to her. But her inquiry served to reawaken my doubts about what had happened with Joseph. Despite the graceful way in which he had accepted his own death, I hadn't been able to disentangle loss from failure.

Was it I who had failed him, or the Simonton theories, or conventional medicine? Or all three? For that matter, what had caused the cancer in the first place? I wondered if anything could have saved him, or prolonged his life in a way he would have found acceptable.

With all my doubts, I remember being convinced of one thing. These things didn't just happen to people, for no reason. There had to be an explanation.

My longtime interest in the possible links between personality factors, stressful life events and cancer was instantly rekindled by my own diagnosis. Tucked away high in one forgotten corner of my bookshelf, I found the copy of the book Joseph had given me, and began to reread it.

This time around, I found I had an entirely different and far more cautious response to these theories, when it was *my* life and *my* personality under scrutiny. But I kept on reading. I felt I owed it to myself to try everything.

When I had first been exposed to the Simonton method, it had seemed logical enough to me that emotional well-being should lead to physical health, and vice versa. *Mens sana in corpore sano*, after all. According to the authors, the possibility of cure or remission was there even in the most dire of circumstances, if only one could come to terms with whatever spiritual and emotional malaise had led to the wild growth of cancer cells in the first place. The book was liberally sprinkled with inspirational stories of this or that terminally ill patient who had defied the odds. Certainly, it was heartening to think that psychological redemption could lead to actual physical survival.

It was only gradually that I began to realize what a double-edged sword this notion could become, inducing guilt and feelings of failure in people already weakened by life-threatening illness. To his credit, Dr. Simonton's present-day counterpart, Dr. Bernie Siegel, is careful to remind his patients that everyone dies, eventually, and that to be "healed" is not necessarily to be "cured."

Many theorists in the field of holistic health, I discovered as I read further, are firmly convinced that cancer patients possess certain psychological characteristics that make them particularly vulnerable to the disease. They are the "nicest" people, the most patient of patients. They don't stand up for themselves, these studies claim, or follow their own dreams, but instead serve the needs of others. They tend to be passive, uncomplaining, and emotionally repressed, concealing their anger under a facade of false cheer.

Looking for myself in this so-called "Type C" profile, I couldn't help but feel disheartened. These were many of the same attributes I'd been struggling with in my own therapy for years. But I thought I'd made real progress. Surely, I was less given to caretaking than I'd been ten years ago. I did let people know how I felt. My husband could attest to that.

And certainly, I was pursuing my dream of becoming a writer. Why, then, had this happened to me?

In examining almost 500 cancer patients in his private practice, psychologist Lawrence LeShan thought he saw a clear pattern of emotional development. While the majority of his patients had suffered losses and deprivation in early childhood, they had gone on to make a successful adaptation in early adulthood through work or a significant relationship, only to lose that crucial role or relationship prior to their illness, which had the effect of reactivating the earlier despair and anger. These emotions were then "bottled up" beneath a saint-like exterior. "To those around them, even people close to them," wrote LeShan, "they seemed to be coping perfectly well . . . but in fact it was the false peace of despair that they felt. They were simply waiting to die. . . . Within six months to eight years, among my patients, the terminal cancer appeared."

Through this line of reasoning, cancer becomes, for those individuals whose personalities and histories predispose them in that direction, the direct biological expression of an unconscious death wish. I thought of my own childhood loneliness and longing for my father's attention, an unhappy first marriage that was so clearly a reiteration of that same longing, and the devastation I'd felt at my father's death. Perhaps my life did fit into LeShan's pattern. "The cancer patient," he concluded, "almost invariably is contemptuous of himself, and of his abilities and possibilities."

At this I balked, for I thought I recognized a pattern here, a certain philosophy of life asserting itself. Does high self-esteem protect one from cancer? People reading LeShan are invited to believe this, as they are invited to believe that expressing emotions freely, especially anger, can serve a preventive function. Fighting for one's rights and achieving one's potential becomes all-important, seen in this light. It would appear that patience, modesty, caretaking, and a reticence to express one's feelings may put one at risk.

In this view, the values of the human potential movement, the "Me" generation, and the New Age, turn out to be not only issues of personal choice and "lifestyle," but matters of life and death as well.

My training in research and evaluation made me suspicious. How could I or anyone determine whether LeShan's findings were valid? The patients in his study were not randomly selected, both they and the investigator knew that they had cancer, and the assessments made were neither systematic nor reproducible. Such conclusions are often based on the case histories and anecdotal reports of researchers who have already formulated their own theories. A control group is rarely, if ever, used. In addition, most studies of this kind turn out to be retrospective. They examine people already diagnosed with cancer, and have the serious flaw that the *effects* of illness—for example, depression—may be confused with the causes.

Knowing all this, I still felt drawn to interpret my situation in terms of LeShan's and the Simontons' theories. I knew it was irrational, but there I was, stuck in the middle, divided between my skepticism on the one hand, and a naive grasping for straws on the other. Increasingly, I found myself obsessively sifting over the events of the past few years, examining my personality for flaws.

Desperate to know, I was caught up in the strong urge many people feel to impute crucial meanings in hindsight to what may well have been only chance or random occurrence, a tendency psychologists have referred to as "effort after meaning." Diagnosed cancer patients, probably because of their concurrent depression, tend to present their pasts in a darker—albeit perhaps more realistic—light, compared to healthy, non-depressed people, who often deny the severity of their problems.

In fact, researcher Martin Seligman, in his fascinating book *Learned Optimism*, has cited evidence that depressed people, though sadder, are wiser—i.e., more observant of events as they actually are. "The pessimist seems to be at the mercy of reality," he wrote, "whereas the optimist has a massive defense against reality that maintains good cheer in the face of a relentlessly indifferent universe."

Reading this, I instantly recognized my own struggle. There was I, a newly hatched and acutely unhappy pessimist trying to climb back into my protective shell, to no avail.

I couldn't escape the conclusion that findings like LeShan's were merely a reflection of what Seligman referred to as "pessimistic explanatory style," activated by the depression that accompanies critical illness, and driven by an "effort after meaning."

As I read further, however, I kept coming across what appeared to be hard scientific evidence that mind-body effects were more than wishful thinking. The Spiegel study at Stanford had shown that breast cancer patients live longer when they attend support groups, although no one could say what aspect of the experience was responsible for this remarkable finding. Perhaps it had nothing to do with the mind at all. Perhaps these women simply became more assertive and received better medical care. Yet other studies showed that a fighting spirit in relation to the cancer, or an attitude of denial—as long as it did not preclude treatment—seemed to be associated with improved survival.

These findings fascinated me. I spent days in a medical library poring through the *Index Medicus*, looking up the original research. I discovered that it's been established repeatedly in the laboratory that immune functioning can be compromised by stress. In human studies, for example, the effects of depression, mourning and helplessness are clearly reflected in temporarily lowered T-cell and NK (natural killer) cell counts. No one, however, has shown conclusively that this sort of effect actually creates a climate within the body where cancer cells, present in all of us and destroyed by our healthy immune systems, reproduce wildly and out of control.

The animal studies intrigued me even more. Learned helplessness in rats, induced by inescapable electric shock, makes the animals more susceptible to tumor growth. Experimental psychologist Robert Ader at the University of Rochester has demonstrated, a number of times, that rats can be conditioned to suppress their immune systems, by feeding them a saccharine drink along with a single injection of cyclophosamide—a.k.a. Cytoxan, an immune-suppressing drug that causes nausea, and incidentally one of the cytotoxic agents that I and most other women with breast cancer receive as part of their chemotherapy protocol. The rats learn fast. After only one such injection, when fed only the drink *without* the drug, the rats suppressed their immune systems anyway.

Dr. Karen Olness at Case Western Reserve, who specializes in self-regulation and conditioning in a medical setting, applied Ader's findings to a young girl with lupus whose treatment required long-term administration of Cytoxan to suppress her overactive immune system. By pairing the drug with the taste of cod liver oil and the smell of roses, they were gradually able to decrease the amount of the drug required for immune system suppression.

Anticipatory nausea, familiar to many cancer patients undergoing chemotherapy, is an example of an unintended conditioned response. A story I'd heard once, probably apocryphal, told of a group of cancer patients who lost their hair, despite the fact that the "chemo" dripped into their veins was only saline solution. It made me wonder if my own lowered blood counts during chemotherapy had been, in part, a conditioned response.

Most people can summon up a story of someone terminally ill who far outlived expectations, who remained alive until an important event—or, conversely, who gave up and succumbed far sooner than expected. Such tales are legion.

Many years ago, I worked for an elderly German historian at Yale who became critically ill while completing the final volume of a history of postwar Europe. Typing and retyping, I shuttled manuscripts back and forth to his hospital room. When the book was finished, the professor managed, with great effort, a trip to Bonn—a first return to Germany since his emigration in the 1930s—to receive an award for his historical work from the German government. It was a great moment, I heard later from the graduate assistant who had accompanied him. That night, the professor died in his sleep.

After suffering a near-fatal heart attack, my father kept himself alive for more than a year, overweight, still smoking, drinking and eating with the same excess he had always enjoyed, until the opening of a major retrospective exhibition of his paintings in San Francisco. With deepest pleasure, he supervised the hanging of the show, attended the opening, gave interviews and talks. Three weeks later, he was dead.

From my reading, it was evident that the biologic mechanisms underlying such dramatic mind-body phenomena as the placebo effect, spontaneous remission, and the influence of the "will to live," have not yet been explained. Researchers are still far from understanding these complex and subtle processes. That they are real seems undeniable, even though the evidence is anecdotal. Why they occur is something else again.

In the midst of all the conflicting evidence, one thing seemed clear to me: fear and the need to control the uncontrollable breed grandiosity and false hopes. The wide popularity of self-help books on healing cancer through imagery, positive thinking and love was proof of this. While a part of me wanted to believe their claims, I came to the conclusion that well-intentioned people, understandably eager for control over life-threatening illness, were jumping the gun by jumping to simplistic conclusions, not only about cure and disease progression but about causation.

The truth of the mind-body equation as regards breast cancer will undoubtedly, when and if we discover it, show itself to be far more complicated than we now suspect, reflecting myriad factors. Breast cancer will prove to be the end result of some intricate mix of controllable and uncontrollable factors relating to heredity, environment, diet, exercise, outlook, emotional stress, and physical factors as yet unguessed, like viruses, disturbances of body chemistry and so forth. Meanwhile, the speculations continue, sensible and otherwise. The desperate scramble for solutions and answers goes on.

The problem is, these ideas affect people deeply as they struggle to come to terms with life-threatening disease. Powerful feelings, both good and bad, go hand-in-hand with these beliefs, as I had discovered first-hand.

Robert Mack, a surgeon with cancer and a proponent of the Simonton method, claimed that, "The patients who survive with cancer or with another catastrophic illness, perhaps even in the face of almost insurmountable odds, seem to be those who have developed a very strong will to live and who value each day, one at a time."

"What about the patients who *don't* survive?" asked Marcia Angell in an editorial in *The New England Journal of Medicine*. "Are they lacking the will to live, or perhaps self-discipline or some other personal attribute necessary to hold cancer at bay? After all, a view that attaches credit to patients for controlling their disease also implies blame for the progression of the disease."

In her critique of the mind-body enthusiasts, Dr. Angell came to the conclusion that theories of physical illness as a reflection of mental state are "largely folklore," and dangerous because they may lead patients to see conventional medical care as irrelevant. "Furthermore," she wrote, "the corollary view of sickness and death as a personal failure is a particularly unfortunate form of blaming the victim. At a time when patients are already burdened by disease, they should not be further burdened by having to accept responsibility for the outcome."

Reading this compassionate view, I felt a sense of relief. I, too, had been feeling guilty for getting so sick, had at times perceived my cancer as a personal failing. "There is mostly shame attached to a disease thought to stem from the repression of emotion," wrote Susan Sontag in her discussion of the myths and metaphors surrounding the disease. "The view of cancer as a disease of the failure of expressiveness condemns the cancer patient: it expresses pity but also conveys contempt . . . the cancer personality is regarded . . . with condescension, as one of life's losers."

Victim-blame is hardly new, of course; the woman who is raped and later chided for dressing provocatively is a familiar example. "Victims are threatening to non-victims," wrote psychologist Shelley Taylor in her eye-opening book, *Positive Illusions*. "If the victimization seems to be due to random forces, it undermines belief in a stable, controllable, beneficent world . . . People therefore try to derogate a victim's behavior as having brought on the victimizing event. . . . When a victim's behavior cannot be blamed, derogation of the victim's character will result."

In other words, those who are healthy have a need to define those who have cancer as different in some crucial way from themselves. This labeling, of which I was equally guilty before my illness, turns on us when we become ill and causes us to blame ourselves, as I did.

"Psychological theories of illness are a powerful means of placing the blame on the ill," Susan Sontag observed. "Patients who are instructed that they have, unwittingly, caused their disease are also being made to feel that they have deserved it."

This kind of thinking is based on a narcissistic assumption of the perfectibility of the self: if I am the right kind of person, I will be healthy.

The reality is, none of us is getting out of here alive—as the saying goes. Today, it's my turn. Tomorrow, or the next day, it may very well be yours.

"A hundred years ago, people might have said God was punishing me . . . " wrote Ruth Shereff, who had ovarian cancer. "Today, my sin is that I . . . do not handle stress properly."

Like the Type A Personality formulation that has been used to predict vulnerability to heart attacks, the notion of stress as a factor in the development of many diseases has entered the public consciousness as a given. In one study, almost half of a group of breast cancer patients believed that their disease had been caused by undue stress in their lives.

Many of the books I was reading seemed to take this notion to extremes. And it is these extremes—not the subtle but intriguing clinical and laboratory observations that represent the current state of what is actually known in the field—that appear to engage the public's interest. The wide readership of books like Bernie Siegel's *Love, Medicine, and Miracles* attests to this.

Such authors are exaggerating a nugget of truth, many believe. "They are taking tiny little observations and stretching them," says Dr. Angell. "It seems very cruel to me to tell patients that if they smiled more or thought better thoughts they would live longer. Imagine how they feel when they get worse anyway!"

Cancer is the physical manifestation of some deep despair, some authors suggest, or a failure to come to terms, on a conscious level, with fundamental and unresolved personality conflicts. Even the location of the tumor is said to have symbolic significance, expressed in the wordless but eloquent language of the body. Often, the disease is thought to actually serve some purpose, or "secondary gain," in the patient's life—a way of getting needs met without having to ask, or even to acknowledge the wish consciously.

It is not hard to apply this kind of thinking to oneself. Most people can point to recent losses, unresolved conflicts, and occasional feelings of helplessness. Moreover, we all tend to feel as if we should have known disaster was about to strike, and somehow be able to do something about it.

Mathematician Massimo Piattelli-Palmarini refers to this phenomenon as "probability blindness." "We all appear to draw a very sharp line between predictability in the future and 'predictability in hindsight,'" he writes. "Once the outcome *is* known, we find it irresistible to assume that we *could* have predicted what was going to happen."

There is another aspect of this kind of reasoning: *Post hoc, ergo propter hoc*—meaning, literally, *after this, therefore because of this*—the fallacy of thinking that a happening which follows another must be its result.

With the wisdom of hindsight, we are impelled to construct a plausible theory to explain the tragic events of our lives. Caught in a depressive mode, we look to our pasts for explanation and find it seething with troubles. Then we mistake sequence for cause, and blame ourselves for not having been able to predict the outcome.

"I toyed with that attitude," writer John Tirman, who had testicular cancer, admitted. "The self-indulgence of believing that I caused my disease by emotional distress or a sloppy life—by not having my 'act' together—is like saying that people are poor because they're stupid and lazy."

The problem is that these theories are as seductive as they are punishing. On the one hand, they appear to hold out the promise of survival, if only the underlying psychological issues can be addressed. But on the other, they hold the victim responsible for her predicament. This produces not only guilt—at least in a perfectionist like me—but an unreasonable panic over any emotional upset or life stress, for fear it will provoke a recurrence.

Dr. Jimmie Holland, chief of psychiatry at Memorial Sloan-Kettering Cancer Center, reports that her patients often worry that "if they are down in the dumps, if they are depressed, they are causing their tumors to grow."

Dealing with the inevitable depression and anxiety that followed my diagnosis, I worried, too, that I was weakening my immune system still further by being so distraught. Should I express my emotions and sink into the grief I was feeling? Wouldn't that just make me more vulnerable? Or should I try to look on the bright side, and risk the damage repressing my emotions might cause?

Frightened, operating on the idea that it was better to try everything, even if unproven, I dutifully practiced my visualization, meditation, relaxation exercises. I worked my way through a shelf full of books with titles like *Cancer as a Turning Point* and *You Can Fight for Your Life*—I even discovered one with the hair-raising title *You Can't Afford the Luxury of a Negative Thought*—before coming to the conclusion that the sense of control these specific theories and techniques offered was far outweighed by the anxiety and self-blame they engendered.

"Why did you invite cancer into your life?" a therapist recommended by Bernie Siegel asked me five minutes into a first interview. His bald presumption, his dazzlingly simplistic assumptions, left me speechless, and I left his office in a blind fury.

But I was still caught in the middle, one foot in each camp, unsure what to believe. Still clinging to the illusion of rational causation, still longing for some means of control, I felt I had to know why this terrible thing had happened to me.

But maybe there was no explanation, after all. Maybe our misfortunes were mere happenstance, a fluke of an impersonal universe. That thought was even more terrifying. I could no more abide the idea of my cancer as random misfortune, over which I had no control at all, than I could the notion of psychological deficit, or perverse, unconscious choice.

Self-pity was not far behind. I began to dread holidays and family gatherings. Envy crept into my relationships. I looked around at friends, engaged in their busy lives. They were healthy. Why me?

As a friend once wryly observed, the only reasonable and realistic answer to the question "Why me?" is "Why *not* me?"

Some years ago, when he was in graduate school, my husband designed a study in which he asked young men with spinal cord injuries how they had been changed by their accidents. A surprising number of them, even the quadriplegics, felt their lives had been improved, despite their disabilities. "I would never have chosen this, but . . . " many of them said.

It's a commonplace to hear cancer patients, particularly women, talk of being able—through the crisis provoked by the disease—to speak up for themselves, often for the first time, and to set their priorities in order.

This is not, of course, to suggest that pain or illness is necessarily ennobling, or that all people "rise to the occasion" when they are so challenged. Life, after all, is not the way it is depicted on those TV problem-of-the-week movies, where simple confrontation yields insight and resolution, all within the neat confines of a two-hour docudrama.

That this reframing of illness is a supremely difficult task is conveyed by the military metaphors used to describe any "battle" with cancer. Like soldiers, patients are said to be "heroic" or "courageous" in their "war" against the disease. Those who show the best chance for survival are the ones who "fight." Tumor cells "invade" the body; the body mounts its "defenses." Even the treatments sound like military actions, complete with the "bombardment" of radiation and chemical "weapons." Under this kind of "assault" or "siege," morale is as easily crushed as the "enemy" disease.

Whatever metaphoric language is chosen, however, it goes without saying that the more catastrophic the crisis, the more urgent the need to mine it for meaning and life-changing potential.

That spring, my treatment complete but my life still in shambles around me, I was sorely in need of such meanings. The anniversary date of my surgery came and went. Unable to write, I kept finding myself browsing through New Age magazines and catalogs, looking for some way to get myself back on track, some process that didn't seem too far out or simplistic.

A trip to the British Isles that my friend Fran and I had planned was canceled. As consolation, the organization that sponsored the trip, a New Age journal called *Earth Star*, offered us press passes to a conference on healing in Boston, entitled "New Medicine and the Biology of Hope."

Perhaps this was a sign, I thought. Most of the authors of my shelf full of books would be there: Norman Cousins, Elizabeth Kubler-Ross, Bernie Siegel, Deepak Chopra, Stephen Locke—even Jon Kabat-Zinn, whose relaxation tapes on closed circuit TV had helped me in the hospital after my mastectomy. The speakers and atmosphere lifted my spirits, and I began to wonder if I had not been too narrow in my thinking, too thin-skinned and defensive. I came home with even more books, and tapes, and brochures.

After that, Fran and I drove down to the Shenandoah Valley of Virginia for a week at a retreat center called the Monroe Institute. In a pleasant dormitory overlooking a pastoral scene of wooded blue hills and fields, we settled in, with twenty others, for six days. We spent most of the time in our "CHEC units," an acronym for "controlled holistic environmental chamber," hi-tech and very comfortable enclosed beds, with sound and light systems as well as recording capabilities—very cozy, but definitely not for claustrophobes. For six to eight hours a day, in a state of almost complete sensory deprivation, we lay in the dark and listened to tapes engineered in the laboratory next door to synchronize the hemispheres of our brains, and thereby induce deep states of relaxation and altered consciousness, a process they refer to as "Hemisync."

Near Charlottesville, Virginia, a community has sprung up under the guidance of Robert Monroe, one-time radio producer and author of *Journeys Out of the Body*, with the focus of exploring and documenting altered states of awareness, OOBEs (out of body experiences), remote viewing, telepathy, and other psychic phenomena.

I had come to this unusual setting via my friend Faith, whose stories of her own recent experience at the Monroe Institute had reawakened my long-term interest in hypnosis, automatic writing, and the use of sound to alter perception.

I left the more bizarre psychic adventures to others in the group. My interest was in exploring my own inner space, and possibly rekindling the creativity I hoped was still smoldering somewhere in there. I didn't care about leaving my body, and I had my doubts that others were really having the OOBEs they reported. But I kept my skepticism to myself.

Some of what they told us seemed to be accurate. There did appear to be discrete levels of awareness, assigned arbitrary numbers by Monroe—three, ten, twelve, twenty-one and so forth. And the Hemisync tones functioned like a shortcut directly into them.

I got to a point where I could go no further. After level twelve, I experienced a sense of endless falling, accompanied by an unpleasant vertigo. As I stayed with it, the faint nausea I felt dissolved into tears. My fear of releasing into my own darkness had become an apt metaphor for a fear of dying. I wept a great deal that day, finally letting myself feel the fear that came over me in waves of uncontrollable trembling.

That night, I slept more soundly than I had in more than a year. The next morning, as the sun rose, I walked down the country road beside the Institute, and a herd of Guernsey cows mooed and clanked their way toward me across a dewy field of wildflowers. I thrust handfuls of grass at their soft muzzles, grinning uncontrollably.

I emerged from my six days at the Monroe Institute refreshed. Cleansed by my catharsis, I was no longer as fearful as I had been before. As for creativity—the wealth of imagery and memories that had welled up inside me in the absence of outside stimulation was encouraging. The whole experience, strange as it was, had opened me up. I was eager for more, for something new. I didn't care how weird it was.

In August, I spent a few days at the Omega Institute, a personal growth center in Rhinebeck, New York, looking for ways to integrate the things I already knew about diet, meditation, and exercise, and put them into practice. The setting was pastoral, the people friendly enough, and the food healthy and well prepared. But there was no new information for me there, nor were there magic answers about the self-discipline required. Still, it was a lovely week, like a summer camp for grownups, and I danced with abandon for the first time in years. I didn't care what I looked like; I knew no one there. It felt wonderful to move my hips, to skip and run and fling my arms high overhead. For a few days, at least, I was friends again with my body.

In an Intensive Journal workshop at a Catholic retreat center in Riverdale with a sweeping view of the Hudson River to the Palisades beyond, I sat in silence with eighty others and wrote about the recent events of my life. Midway through the four days, I found myself in a dialogue with my illness, personified in my fantasy as a rather smug, high-handed internal voice. I ranted, I raved. I asked unanswerable questions, transcribing this inner conversation as if it were a scene in a play.

"Why are you in my life?" I wanted to know.

"I present you with these challenges," my cancer replied. "To live life fully, never knowing how much time you may have remaining. To embrace the experience of brushing close to death, having undergone painful and difficult treatment. To accept yourself as a woman again, without a breast, and with all the changes of menopause. To take responsibility for doing everything you can do to achieve optimal health. To live with the realization that even if you do all that you can, it may still not be enough, for you cannot control everything, or even the most important things."

"Are you in any way a punishment," I asked, "an expression of guilt?"

"You are always looking for fault in yourself," was the answer. "Naturally, you look for that in me, too."

I returned home. The summer was over, and I'd had more than my fill of workshops and institutes. I felt gorged, as if I'd sampled too many of the sweet desserts from a buffet table.

Each of these experiences had been useful, even inspiring, at the time. But the glow quickly faded. I kept wandering off any path I tried, uncertain that it would take me anywhere. Though I longed to identify myself with like-minded others, I was mistrustful of cults or organized groups who claimed to have answers. Being alone in the woods, making my own way, was preferable to walking a heavily trodden trail. But on my own, I got nowhere. Bushwhacking through the underbrush, I was easily lost and distracted, ending up walking in circles. And so I'd try something new, something else, in the hope that this would be "it."

I was always disappointed. Even as I flirted with New Age pieties, they revealed themselves to me as such, mere techniques for feeling better.

I wanted more. I wanted "truth." Certainty. Answers. "The final belief," the poet Wallace Stevens wrote, "is to believe in a fiction which you know to be a fiction." My problem seemed to be that I was incapable of any leap of faith into this "final belief."

Or so I thought. What I was really looking for, I see now that I've begun to write again, was not belief at all, but the pleasures of language. I was in need of poetry, not techniques.

And something else—something so obvious and yet so difficult it had eluded me through all my frantic searching: I needed to accept what had happened to me.

SEVEN

Outward Appearances

Her self
lost to herself
she has gone
to confront the high
priestess, Necessitas.
— DARCY GOTTLIEB,
"The Weeping Place"

P ARALLEL TO THE rest of my medical treatment, but arguably less crucial, the making of my new breast had often commanded center stage in my psyche. At last, after a year and a half, the process was nearing completion.

My first glimpse of a reconstructed breast "in the flesh" had been on the eve of my mastectomy, when I was still trying to decide what to do.

I only saw Laura once, but she left a lasting impression on me. She had been waiting outside for us that sunny late April afternoon, sitting on the stoop of her building in Larchmont and watching her two small dogs sniff and scamper around the walk.

A slim, pretty blond with tousled hair, she stood as Tom and I approached the entrance to her apartment building, greeting me with level gray eyes and a strong handshake.

"Are you Musa?" she asked, and we introduced ourselves. We had spoken on the telephone the night before, at some length, about plastic surgery, and she had offered to show me the results of her reconstruction.

Tom hesitated before entering the building, uncertain of his role in this rather odd visit. "Should I wait for you down here?" he asked, looking at me.

"No, no," she said. "Come on up. It's okay."

We sat, she and Tom and I, on her living room couch and chatted awkwardly for a few minutes.

"Well," Laura said finally, casting me a meaningful glance. "Shall we?"

I followed her into the bedroom, and she shut the door. I watched as she unbuttoned her blouse and took it off. A very sexy, almost see-through white lace bra barely concealed her breasts. She looked perfectly normal, in every way.

"Can you tell which one it is?" Laura asked.

I peered at her bosom, examining it as closely as I dared.

At first glance, there seemed to be no difference between the two sides, but then I saw a thin scar through the transparent fabric, rising from the bottom of her right breast to the nipple and encircling it. I pointed to the other breast. "It's got to be that one," I said. "But I only could tell because of the mastopexy scar."

She reached around to unhook her bra and stood before me, her large breasts bare now, hands on hips. "Don't be shy," she said. "I don't mind. You can touch it, if you want."

I stared. The illusion was remarkable, the scar barely visible, the shape almost perfect, although less pendulous, matching the other, real breast, which had been "lifted," the mastopexy to which I'd referred a moment before. It was one thing to see the plastic surgeon's slides, quite another to confront a reconstructed breast in the flesh. Gently, I poked at it. It was warm, and somewhat firmer to the touch than I'd expected. While the areola matched its twin quite well, the nipple was of normal skin color. I asked about that.

"I haven't had them tattoo it yet," she said. "I guess I should, but I sort of like the two-toned effect."

"And how does it feel to you?"

She leaned over to fit her breasts back into the lacy bra, then reached to hook it behind her back. "Well, the surgery was a pain to go through, but I'm really happy I did it now. My breasts are very important to me."

"What I meant was, how does it actually feel, physically, to have the implant in your body?"

"I don't know how to answer that," she said, looking a little puzzled. "It doesn't hurt or anything."

"Does it feel natural?"

"Well, no, not exactly. You can tell it's not you, if that's what you mean." She began to button her shirt.

"Doesn't it seem . . . well, alien?"

"Not to me."

There was a moment of silence. "So," she said. "Your surgery's tomorrow?"

I nodded. "I've read a lot and talked with other women, but I'm still pretty terrified."

"Of course. I was, too. Everyone is, you can't help that." She cupped her breasts in her hands for a moment, then let them go. "A year from now, you're going to be very happy you decided to do this."

"If I look half as good as you do, I'm sure I will be," I said.

"It makes all the difference. You'll see. I waited over a year and a half to have it done. I kept putting it off—I didn't want more surgery, I wasn't sure, the time wasn't right, whatever." Laura sighed, remembering. "Mostly, I guess I just wanted to be done with having cancer, and so I'd try to ignore how I looked. But then every time I got dressed, or took a shower, or my prosthesis rode up to my chin, I would be reminded of it. Now, I wonder why I put it off so long. I wish I'd had immediate reconstruction, like you."

"Why didn't you?"

"My breast surgeon was opposed to it. He was from the old 'one thing at a time' school. He made me feel as if saving my life was the only thing I should be thinking about."

Back in the living room, Tom had been playing with Laura's two Staffordshire terriers. One looked old enough to be the other's mother, and so I asked if that was the case.

Laura laughed. "No, they're not related. I've had Cecie for years. After my mastectomy, I decided I had to have another dog, and so I bought Totie here." As we approached the outer door of the apartment, both dogs began to bark. She picked them up and tucked one under each arm. "It was funny. I didn't put it together until later why it was, but suddenly, it was like I had to have two of everything. Everything had to be in pairs. I even started rearranging all the furniture so it would be symmetrical."

When we got home, I approached Tom with a request. "I want you to take a picture of how my breasts look now, before the surgery."

"You what?" He stared at me incredulously.

"I want a 'before' picture, so I can remember what I looked like."

"Won't that just make you more aware of the loss?"

"I got the idea from those slides we saw at the plastic surgeon's office," I said. "But they're just the final outcome. It would have been better to have seen what those women looked like before, and during the reconstruction. I thought it would be good to document each stage of the process."

"Why? Who would you show it to?"

"I don't know. Probably no one. I just want a record kept."

In the back of my lingerie drawer is a small white envelope with half a dozen photographs of my chest, taken over the course of a year and a half—before, during and after my reconstructive surgery.

Some months before my diagnosis, the writer Philip Roth, who had been a good friend of my father's, had called and asked me to come to his apartment to look at a set of sketches my father had made in response to Roth's satiric novel, *The Breast*, when it was first published in the early 1970s. In Kafka's famous short story, *The Metamorphosis*, the protagonist, Gregor Samsa, wakes up one morning to find himself transformed into a man-sized cockroach. In *The Breast*, a man wakes up one morning to find himself transformed into a giant, disembodied female breast.

Philip Roth wanted to discuss republication of his book with me, using these drawings as illustrations and an elegiac essay about his friendship with my father as a preface. The drawings themselves were disappointing. Done on typing paper, few of them were fully realized. They had not, I suspected, ever been intended for anyone else's eyes, representing only a ribald and whimsical reading of a friend's book, rather than finished work. So it was with some reluctance that I agreed to the project, approving the half dozen or so drawings that were of acceptable quality.

Shortly thereafter, Roth left his publisher of many years, and I heard nothing more of the project until a year later, when he called to tell me that *Vanity Fair* was publishing his introductory essay, with several of the Guston drawings.

We exchanged news of our recent medical crises: his coronary bypass surgery, my mastectomy. It had only been a month since his surgery, and the experience still dominated his life; he spoke of the sudden shortness of breath, the emergency intervention, the kindness of the medical personnel, how it had felt to come face to face with his mortality in such an abrupt fashion. I listened to him talk, but all I could think about was how bizarre the fundamental image and premise of his earlier novel seemed to me, now that I had experienced the reality of a disembodied breast firsthand.

A chain of associations came to me as I sat in my kitchen that day, after hanging up the telephone. I thought of how it had felt to read the pathology report after my mastectomy, and see my breast described as "the specimen received," covered by an "ellipse of tan soft skin measuring 24 x 8 cm." I thought of a late medieval painting I'd seen once of one of the Catholic martyrs, bearing her severed breasts on a platter as a grotesque offering of piety. I thought of the harsh, angry words women sometimes use to describe the results of mastectomy—mutilation, amputation, disfigurement. I put my hands on my chest, feeling the soft mound on the left, the nipple rising to my touch, and the hard bulge on the right where the tissue expander was stretching my benumbed skin to create a replica. My fingers strayed downward to trace the taught rope of scar tissue that ran from navel to pubic bone, the external evidence of the more inward and invisible loss of my uterus.

What a strange progression it was, from Roth's exploration of the breast as a male fantasy object to these bleak ruminations on the loss of my sexual parts.

Going into the bedroom, I rummaged in my dresser drawer for the envelope of pictures of my chest in various stages of surgery and reconstruction. In black ink, I gave it the ironic label it seemed to require: "The Breast."

By then, I had been completely "inflated" and was awaiting the end of my chemotherapy and my oncologist's word that my blood count had revived enough to undergo surgery. All summer and fall I had visited the plastic surgeon's office every week or two for injections of saline solution. I looked forward to these visits. The office was plush, the receptionists and nurses friendly and considerate. And, most important, something positive was happening there. I might leave with my skin painfully tight, and my pectoral muscles in spasm where they stretched over the implant, but these minor discomforts paled by comparison with the imagined outcome.

The dream of a perfectly shaped breast hung tantalizingly in the not-too-distant future. Over the months of my chemotherapy, the reconstruction had come to have a much larger symbolic meaning than it merited, as I understood only later. Dimly, I realized that I was expecting an awful lot from that pound of flesh, salt water and silicone gel: not only the appearance of normalcy, but normalcy itself.

What I ended up with, of course, was quite different. Throughout the process, the reconstructed breast retained its power as a metaphor for my whole sense of self, but the symbol itself was becoming increasingly mixed. I was the same person — sort of, until you looked closely — but my inner landscape had radically changed. Never had the division between outward appearance and inner experience been more sharply defined.

Often, I went directly from the plastic surgeon's office to a small salon on an upper floor of a Madison Avenue office building that sold what was unappetizingly referred to as "Mastectomy Supplies." The routine was always the same. I would strip to my bra with the pockets in it, and the woman who owned the store would scurry away to find something to recreate the symmetry my latest expansion had unbalanced.

While she was gone, my attention was always drawn to the stack of prostheses in what looked like shoe boxes in front of the mirror. With fascination and a bit of distaste, I would pick up and hold one of the surprisingly heavy, gelatinous pink things in my hand. Despite their strangeness, the prostheses did seem soft and natural feeling, at least compared with the rigid grapefruit-half on my chest. More than once, I found myself wondering if I wouldn't have been happier leaving well enough alone.

One of the drawbacks of immediate reconstruction is that a woman makes the choice to do it with only a partial and conceptual knowledge of the alternative, and at a time when she is under great emotional pressure. She never really knows what it would be like for her to have only a scar where her breast once was, or to wear a prosthesis.

Whatever its cosmetic desirability, an implant presents a set of problems of its own. Linda Dackman expressed it most eloquently and graphically in her book, *Up Front*, when she wrote: "When I woke up after reconstruction, I felt married to a stranger. And it was not merely occupying my bed; it was permanently embedded in my body!"

There were times when I longed to be rid of the strange insensate mound formed by the tissue expander that sat where my right breast used to be. But I kept on hoping, fantasizing how it would be different once the reconstruction was complete.

Over the previous few months, I had accumulated quite a collection of falsies and breast pads to accommodate my changing shapes and sizes. After I had stuffed the latest set of pads into my bra, I would don the thin top the salon owner kept on a hook and flatten it against my chest so we would survey the results together. "Pretty good," she would say. "Can I interest you in a bathing suit? Another bra?"

Finally, I was fully inflated—in fact, overinflated. Unclothed, I looked bizarre, with this angry-looking growth projecting from my chest wall, bisected laterally by the long, thin scar of the mastectomy. It was so large that I had to wear pads on the other side for balance. The overinflation was supposed to create a pocket under the skin into which the permanent implant would fit more loosely, and therefore, more naturally. I was eager for the next stage, but I had to wait until at least a month after the completion of my chemotherapy. Because of the low white blood counts induced by cancer-killing drugs, there is an increased risk of infection during surgery. Even my dentist was reluctant to work on me at the time—just as well, I decided, having been reduced to tears during a routine, if somewhat painful, teeth cleaning. It was shocking to me how vulnerable I still felt.

I set the date for the "exchange" surgery, in which the tissue expander would be replaced by a permanent implant. As the date approached and the effects of chemo began to wear off, I found myself actually looking forward to the surgery. I couldn't wait to be rid of the rock-hard bulge created by the tissue expander, which was nothing like the teardrop shape of a mature natural breast.

In the same surgery, I had also decided to have a mastopexy done on the other breast, which had drooped with age, so that the results would be more symmetrical. The mastopexy, or breast "lift," is an operation that removes a portion of stretched out skin via a keyhole-shaped incision—the same incision used for breast reduction—leaving a long scar beneath the breast, up the midline and around the nipple and areola, which are actually moved to a point higher up on the breast.

While I was looking forward to the outcome of the surgery, the prospect of returning to the hospital, less than a year after my mastectomy, made me uneasy. The worst part turned out not to be the surgery itself, or the hospital stay, but something that occurred before I even checked in. At the pre-surgical testing, three lab technicians, each attempting to draw blood, ended up having to poke me seven times as one vein after another in my left arm collapsed.

As often happens, my chemotherapy had all but destroyed the superficial veins of my other arm. As a consequence, the once-simple act of drawing blood became an ordeal. Because of an increased risk of infection, a woman who has had her axillary lymph nodes removed is advised not to have injections or blood drawn from the mastectomy side.

That day, I longed for my oncologist's nurse, with her gentle touch and sixth sense about where a viable vein might be hiding. I flinched and snapped at the technicians, making them nervous. By the end of my time there, I was again in tears.

Once I checked in, however, I was fine. I shared a hospital room with three other women, two of them scheduled for breast surgery with my plastic surgeon, and the third to have a face lift. Within a short period of time, we had dismissed our various husbands, and settled in to compare notes. One woman, an unmarried teacher in her early forties, was to have the same surgery as I was, immediately before me the following day. The other woman, a fiftyish homemaker from Queens, was having a "touch up," as she called it, to a flap operation done some months before.

Although I had heard of the so-called "tram flap" surgery, I had never seen the results, and was quite curious. Before I could ask, she offered to show us what she looked like.

In the form of reconstructive surgery she'd had, the woman's own tissue is used to reconstruct a breast. A long incision is made across the lower abdomen and a wide crescent-shaped wedge of skin and fatty tissue is removed (in what is often referred to as a "tummy tuck") and tunneled beneath the skin—complete with its own blood supply and tethered by the rectus abdominus muscle—to the surgical site of the mastectomy, where it is shaped and sutured into place. This intricate surgery takes several hours, and carries a small but significant risk of infection, a longer recovery period, more extensive scarring, and in some cases, muscle weakness in the abdomen. The principal advantage is that there is no foreign substance implanted in the body, no "stranger" to whom one is "married."

Despite the cost and arduousness of this procedure, and the relative simplicity of implant surgery, flap procedures are being used with greater frequency these days, often at the time of mastectomy. Fears of silicone-related illness have contributed to this trend. Besides the tram flap, there is "lat" flap surgery, which uses the latissimus muscle from the back to form the breast, as well as various "free flap" procedures, commonly using tissue from the buttocks, which involve complete reattachment and delicate microsurgery. I had rejected these options, fearing the lengthy surgery and long recovery period.

Drawing the curtain around her bed, the woman pulled up her nightgown and exposed her body. The scars were particularly prominent on her torso, since she'd had some sort of allergic response to the materials used for the sutures. That was why she had come in for this surgery, she told me, to "fix up" her scars. A prominent rope-like red scar ran from hip to hip across her belly, and circled her reconstructed breast. I couldn't help wondering if a simple mastectomy would have been less disfiguring.

My surgery went without a hitch. I was awake and alert soon afterwards, and in some pain, not from the implant side, which was mostly deadened to sensation anyway, but from the mastopexy. As soon as I could, I got up and went into the bathroom to see for myself what the implant looked like. By probing with my fingers, I already knew that it was soft and natural-feeling—at least from the outside.

After having looked at it from all angles, I decided that it looked just like a real breast—of a modestly-endowed sixteen-year-old! How strange it appeared, fastened to my aging body. It was completely "pert" and upstanding—a detail-less Barbie Doll of a boob without its nipple, the kind of breast shape I remembered coveting as an adolescent. How ironic that I should be granted this perfect shape now, in this way, when I no longer viewed it as an ideal form.

What it lacked, besides a nipple, was the normal graceful sag of a mature woman. Who designs these things? I wondered, darkly. If most women with breast cancer were over forty, with the effects of gravity clearly in evidence, why give them these teenage fantasy breasts? There was no crease beneath it; I could not have passed, as a friend delicately put it, the "pencil test." Later, I realized that the stretchability of my skin around the tissue expander determined this shape, at least to some extent. Other women, with more pliable skin and less scar tissue formation, obtained a more cosmetic result.

Still, this new softness was gratifying. I wouldn't be assaulting my friends with a blunt object every time I hugged them anymore.

Wincing, I uncovered the other breast, which had been loosely bandaged to protect the stitches from rubbing against my hospital gown. A small thicket of black sutures surrounded the areola and nipple, which had been moved up on my breast and made smaller. It now pointed outward, rather than downward. The fold beneath my left breast concealed a six-inch-long incision and more sutures, and a fine line of stitches connected them. I could see that when the stitches healed and my breast no longer resembled a patchwork quilt, the shape would be pleasing. Judging from the pain I felt when I touched my nipple, there had been no loss of sensation—as sometimes happens.

And yet, I couldn't deny my disappointment. But what, after all, had I expected? To be magically restored to my former self? To have a new and glamorous set of knockers I could show off with pride, as if having cancer had merely provided this sterling opportunity for self-improvement?

Rather than questioning these naive hopes, I resolved to defer judgment. "The Breast" was still an unfinished work, after all. Maybe with a nipple, the illusion would be more complete.

By the time I was ready for the nipple reconstruction five months later, I still had an angry-looking raised scar around my left areola and beneath my breast that made it painful to wear a bra. "Give it time," my plastic surgeon said, and prescribed what looked like scotch tape, impregnated with cortisone, to paste over the scars.

The nipple reconstruction was a simple skin-grafting procedure done under local anesthesia in Day Surgery, where I'd had my biopsy done. Naked to the waist, I sat in the cold operating room while the surgeon held a ruler to my breast, cocked his head and squinted. He drew two concentric circles at the spot on my reconstructed breast where he thought the areola and nipple should be, then handed me a mirror. "What do you think?" he asked. "Does the placement look right to you?"

"I guess so," I said, doubtfully. The bullseye in black magic marker on my Barbie doll side did seem to be at the same level as the other side. He went off to scrub for the surgery, and I lay down and let them drape me. A thin, doughnut-shaped piece of skin would be taken from under my right arm, adjacent to my mastectomy scar. Grafted onto my skin, this would form the areola. Often the skin for the graft is taken from the inner thigh or some other part of the body that has a darker pigmentation, but I had welcomed the idea of not having an additional scar to contend with. The nipple itself would be fashioned from the skin already there, drawn up through the hole in the middle of the graft. Both nipple and areola could be tattooed later for a better color match.

The whole procedure was swift and painless. The only surprise of this surgery was the odd "pom-pom bandage," actually sewn onto the surgical site, to hold the graft underneath in place so it could "take." Since the nerves in the area the surgeon was working on had been severed by the mastectomy incision, there was no sensation associated with it at all. In fact, I had to be careful not to jostle my "pom-pom" while it was healing, since I couldn't feel a thing.

"Oh, my goodness," cried the owner of the mastectomy supplies salon, when she saw me the next day. "This will be a challenge." She hurried off to look for another pad.

When the bandages came off and a week or so had passed, I could see that the graft had been successful. My new breast was no longer "blind"; now it had an eye, a focal point. But when I touched the nipple, the only thing I felt was my hand, as if I were touching someone else.

"Will I ever have any feeling there?" I asked the plastic surgeon.

"You might. Some women do get sensation in their nipples," he told me.

Except for the tattooing, and a slight "revision" of the shape of my new nipple, I was now "finished." I felt let down. So this was it. Nothing more to look forward to. This was what I could expect from my reconstruction.

Why was I still disappointed? It looked okay, I thought. Not perfect, but okay. I could see myself being able to change in the locker room of my health club, and not drawing curious or horrified glances. I looked passable in my clothes, and was far more self-conscious about my excess weight than about my reconstructed breast. I even had cleavage again, in a bathing suit.

"There is hope and expectation in this form of immediate reconstruction," as Linda Dackman points out, "as long as there is anticipation." Intellectually, I knew perfectly well that all that had been resolved was the partial improvement of the right half of my chest. Emotionally, it was another story—although I only became aware of each dashed expectation as it surfaced in the form of a disappointment.

One such moment came when I asked Tom to caress my new breast as a part of our lovemaking—we had both avoided it up to that point—and discovered that I hated the sensation—or rather, the lack of it—of being touched there. Far from being pleasurable, his fondling only served as an unwelcome reminder that this new appendage was breast-like only in appearance. This came as a shock to me, for I had come to enjoy touching it myself, feeling its reassuring roundness and heaviness in my hand. Somehow, with the sensations in my fingers, the numbness hadn't bothered me. But when Tom touched me there, it was as if he had kissed me on the mouth when my lips were deadened with novocaine. My new breast, on which so much time and money and hope had been expended, felt like dead meat. My sense of loss had never been more acute than it was at that moment.

It is hard for me to make sense of why this all mattered so much, when much more—my life, in fact—was at stake. My breasts had never been beautifully shaped or exquisitely sensitive erotic playgrounds, after all. While my husband didn't neglect them, they were hardly the focus of our lovemaking. Why then, I had to ask myself, had the process of reconstruction occupied such a central role in my psyche over the past two years?

In part, I believe that it acted like a lightning rod, to draw the heat and fire from other losses. In the economy of the psyche, one thing often stands for many. Reconstructive surgery became the single positive visual symbol that might stave off the desexualization process that had begun years before with my hysterectomy. The loss of my uterus, my breast, my female hormones—and with that, the decline in sexual interest and responsiveness—all these had converged in this one arena.

Since my diagnosis, my womanhood had been called into question, not by others, for my outward physical appearance, scars notwithstanding, hadn't altered all that much. But my own inner sense of femaleness had changed profoundly. This had come about not from a single trauma, but through an accretion of related concerns, each of which had some bearing on this basic issue of sexual body image. Infertility, hysterectomy, weight gain, aging, menopause—all of these factored into the equation.

The mastectomy was only the last and final straw, just as the reconstruction had become the single and magical cure.

Somewhere in the ordeal of dealing with cancer, I seemed to have lost the kind of confidence that flows naturally from being healthy and fit and attractive, a precious commodity that had never been mine in great supply in the first place. Instead, I was carrying around that familiar secret that so many American women live with: I didn't really like my body. In so many ways, it was less than what I wished it to be. Every day I found myself documenting its flaws: the increase in my clothing size, the varicose veins in my legs, the aching of my joints from chemotherapy induced "polyarthralgia," the diagnostic label my rheumatologist had used, a fancy term for "it hurts everywhere."

I found myself living in a state of perpetual envy and longing—not for the ideal female form, for that was well beyond my reach, but for my own lost self, as I used to be, the woman who could hike and dance and lose weight and feel the spontaneous flush of sexual desire.

My mother's reaction to her own aging was an object lesson for me in coming to terms with all of this. Her self-consciousness over her hunched back, her wrinkled skin and falling hair, made her reclusive, unwilling to spend time in the company of others. Her impaired memory and word-finding skills were an embarrassment to her. "They'll think, what a foolish old woman she is," my mother would say, or else, when trying to decide whether or not to attend a party or an opening, "They don't want to see a bag of skin and bones like me." I was quick to reassure her, seeing so clearly, as I did, that it was not others who would sit in judgment of her, but she herself.

But I was clearly my mother's daughter. Those seeds of self-doubt and insecurity were sowed deep within me, too, awaiting opportunities to grow and flourish.

Due at least in part to my mother's influence, I have never been particularly inclined toward the various time-consuming and tortuous practices that women engage in to make themselves attractive. Loose-fitting cotton clothing is what I usually wear. I rarely bother with makeup. Comfortable walking shoes win out over heels every time. Sacrificing glamour for functionality has never been a question for me. Not being a purist, however, I do make a few concessions here and there: I shave my legs, I wear lipstick. To my mind, the price I pay in occasional feelings of inferiority in the presence of well-turned-out, glamorous women is well worth the savings in time and comfort.

Were it socially acceptable for a single-breasted woman not to wear a prosthesis in public, and were I able to do so without undue self-consciousness, there's no question in my mind that this is the choice that would feel most natural to me.

Some brave women do make this choice. After her mastectomy, black feminist and lesbian poet Audre Lorde chose not to wear a prosthesis, considering it to be a "cosmetic sham." The concealment of breast cancer in this way bothered her deeply: "I believe that socially sanctioned prosthesis is merely another way of keeping women with breast cancer silent and separate from one another.

"This emphasis upon the cosmetic after surgery reinforces this society's stereotype of women," she wrote, "that we are only what we look [like] or appear [to be], so this is the only aspect of our existence we need to address."

The nurse in her surgeon's office had implored Lorde to wear a prosthesis, saying it was bad for "office morale" if she did not. But she refused. She didn't want to conceal her loss. Far from it. "I refuse to have my scars hidden or trivialized behind lambswool or silicone gel. I refused to be reduced in my own eyes or in the eyes of others from warrior to mere victim . . . "

Lorde found that, for her, a prosthesis formed a barrier between herself and a necessary confrontation with mortality, as it isolated her from other women like herself. As might be expected, Lorde was even more vehemently opposed to breast reconstruction, seeing it as a dangerous and potentially cancer-promoting surgery pushed by those who wish to perpetuate the objectification of women.

Almost a year after my diagnosis, a woman in my support group lent me a copy of Lorde's 1980 book, *The Cancer Journals*, which includes her essay on the politics of prosthesis and reconstruction. My immediate reaction was defensive. I didn't like being told I had been duped into a dangerous complacency. But was she right? Had I bowed to the male doctors' biases, to the cultural expectations of what constituted a woman, rather than heroically carving my own path, as she had?

That was too complicated a question to have a simple answer. It was important that I affirm my own choices, I decided, and not worry about the feminist "correctness" of my decision. It put me in mind of a time, back in the seventies, when shaving one's legs or wearing makeup was considered reactionary and anti-feminist in some circles.

Nevertheless, I had to admit that Lorde's analysis of reconstruction struck some painful chords. "When I mourn my right breast," Lorde wrote, "it is not the appearance of it I mourn, but the feeling and the fact."

I knew exactly what she meant. It was this precise discrepancy that had caused me so much anguish, trying to reconcile the gap between what I felt and how I looked. Only after I was able to disentangle the subjective and objective aspects of the surgery, and pare my expectations down to fit the realities at hand, was I able to relax and begin to enjoy the real benefits of the reconstruction—which are, when all is said and done, principally ones of convenience.

It resembles a breast, and I am happy for that. Certainly, it is convenient for dressing. Bathing suits and nightgowns, and even low-cut dresses are never a problem. Because of the surgical correction of what doctors call "ptosis," the droop that is the prerogative of gravity and age to a woman's breasts, I can even do something I haven't been able to do in years: I can now wear a T-shirt with no bra and get away with it—as long as my real nipple doesn't become erect, that is!

All in all, my disappointments with reconstruction have had far less to do with appearance, and more with how it has felt to incorporate this "stranger" into my body. That, and of course the reality that it didn't and couldn't magically "undo" the fact that I'd had breast cancer, as I somehow assumed it would.

Sometimes, I must admit, I do find myself wondering if Audre Lorde wasn't right, and I long for what I imagine would be the clean, spare feeling of nothing but skin and muscle and ribs. My skin is numb beneath my arm and for a few inches on either side of my scar, across the entire front of the reconstructed breast. Although this would be the case without reconstruction, too, having the artificial breast there exaggerates this loss of sensation, stretching the area, and making it both more prominent, and more poignant, considering the location of this normally sensitive and erotic part.

There are other regrets. I'd like to be able to sleep comfortably on my stomach again. I'd like to be able to hug someone without self-consciousness. Most of all, I'd like to feel the weight of my husband's body on mine when we are making love without this sack of silicone and saline between us. What Laura hadn't been able to articulate when I asked her, the subjective "feel" of a reconstructed breast, has become of crucial importance—not how it looks, but the day-to-day pleasures, discomfort, and risks of living with an implant.

Despite all the doubts about my reconstruction, all the freight the plastic surgery had to bear and all the dashing of illusions, I do not regret having made the choice. After a period of adjustment, I have found myself most of the time delighted to be able to dispense with an external prosthesis. It is so much easier. For the most part, I have made my peace with it. My implant no longer seems alien to me, but a real part of myself.

The concept of "ego alien" was once graphically explained to me by a psychologist friend, who instructed me, by way of demonstration, to spit in a glass, then drink it. I made a face at the idea. Why, my friend asked, did a body fluid normally carried in the mouth suddenly became distasteful outside the boundaries of the body? I had no answer. What happened with my implant seems to have been just the opposite—that by carrying a foreign substance within the confines of my own skin, I had incorporated it as a part of myself. It had taken almost a year and a half, but at last, I was finished with my reconstruction.

But this respite, as it turned out, was short-lasting. Reports about serious health questions concerning breast implants began to surface in the national media in December of 1990, when Connie Chung did a segment on the evening news about an implant called "Même," manufactured by a company called Surgitek, a subsidiary of Bristol-Myers Squibb Company. The implant was coated with a polyurethane foam that ostensibly reduces capsular contracture, one of the more common and troublesome side effects of breast implants. This condition, which can sometimes be corrected surgically, occurs when a tight capsule of scar tissue forms around an implant, causing the reconstructed breast to become unusually firm and sometimes distorted in appearance.

Another problem that can occur involves the leakage of silicone gel, which can "bleed" in small amounts through the intact membrane of an implant. Exposure is even more likely from a ruptured implant, where larger quantities of silicone gel are in direct contact with body tissue. While nothing has been conclusively proven, it seems that silicone gel can be taken up by the white blood cells and circulated throughout the lymphatic system, causing enlarged lymph glands and forming silicone granulomas. Silicone gel has been implicated for the role it may play in a number of autoimmune and connective tissue diseases, like rheumatoid arthritis, systemic lupus erythematosus and scleroderma. No one has conclusively demonstrated a causal connection, but the anecdotal evidence continues to mount, and the longterm effects of silicone gel in the human body are still unknown.

For the first time, the FDA has required that breast implant manufacturers provide conclusive proof of the safety of their products, which have been around since 1960 and were "grandfathered in" in 1976, allowing them to remain on the market without further evidence of safety. In 1982, the FDA stated that "breast implants present a potential unreasonable risk of injury," and recommended Class III regulatory classification, which demanded further testing. This was never implemented. Finally, in 1990, the FDA issued a requirement for "pre-market approval" of these devices.

The furor over the "Même" and "Replicon" implants revolves around the contention that the polyurethane foam coating the surface breaks down in the body into TDA, a known carcinogen that has been proven, in animal studies, to cause cancerous tumors.

Eva, from my support group, who had one of these implants, researched everything she could about the risks of breast implants. What she discovered spurred me to do the same for my implant, an expandable mixture of saline and silicone.

What I gleaned from my readings and phone calls was sobering. From the Command Trust Network, a national implant registry and information clearinghouse, came hair-raising stories of women with years of mysterious, debilitating symptoms. From the literature they sent, I learned that there are more than two million women in the United States with silicone breast implants, placed there either for reconstructive surgery after cancer or for simple breast augmentation. I learned that while plastic surgeons have been using implants filled with silicone gel for more than twenty years, there are in fact no valid longterm studies on its interaction with body tissue—in this form, at least. Because it caused cancer in rats, injectable silicone gel—once freely used by plastic surgeons—was banned years ago. I learned that it is often difficult to tell when the Silastic envelope enclosing silicone gel implants ruptures, spilling the contents into the scar capsule.

In 1991, in New York State, a multimillion-dollar lawsuit was won by a patient diagnosed with ovarian cancer, after a pathologist claimed to have found silicone in her ovaries that had "migrated" from her breast implant.

My doctors, however, advised a wait-and-see approach. "There's no real evidence to support these claims, you know," my plastic surgeon said, when I went to see him in a panic. "That pathologist is known for his testimony in malpractice cases. I wouldn't use this implant if I didn't have utmost confidence in it. Besides, it's ninety percent saline solution."

"Yes, but it's the other ten percent I worry about. And with this polyarthralgia I have—"

"What does your rheumatologist say?"

"The same thing you did. That I should hold off. That the possibility my aches and pains are related to the implant is extremely remote. But I think I'd continue to worry about the silicone, never knowing if the implant had ruptured, or what could take place if that happened."

"I could build you a breast from your own tissue, you know."

"That seems like too much surgery to me. Is that my only alternative?"

"Well, no, there's a textured all-saline implant available now, that I've been using for women who are worried about the risks of silicone."

And so I decided on an exchange of implants, although I was far from eager about undergoing another operation. It seemed like the best compromise. This time, as I approached the surgery, I was cognizant of the risks involved. I knew full well I faced some possibility of capsular contracture, scarring, infection, bleeding, skin necrosis, and displacement, leakage or rupture of the implant itself. I knew that the implant would not last forever, that someday I would face another decision and another operation.

With these new and worrisome developments, has it all been worth it, to regain a shape that is, at best, a mere simulation of my former self? I don't know. It depends on what day you ask me.

EIGHT

Journey into Self

I am a man: little do I last
and the night is enormous.
But I look up:
the stars write.
Unknowing, I understand:
I too am written,
and at this very moment
someone spells me out.
— OCTAVIO PAZ

IN OCTOBER OF 1990, almost a full year after the end of my chemotherapy, I found myself halfway around the world, lying flat on my back in a rutted field outside of Gyantse, Tibet. It was a moonless night, and the dome of sky above was thick with stars. At 14,000 feet, the air was thin, and the barley stubble pressed uncomfortably against my jacket. From somewhere close by came the howling of dogs.

It had been five days since I'd had a bath or a meal worth eating. Walking up a flight of steps left me breathless from the altitude, my nose and eyes were irritated from the dust and extreme dryness, and my body ached from bouncing around on unpaved roads. But at that moment I didn't care. How remarkable, I thought, just to be here, on the roof of the world. Above me, the familiar constellations were obscured by the milky abundance of distant stars. Everything seemed so completely alien, yet I felt at peace.

I was away from home nearly six weeks, passport and around-the-world ticket from British Airways in my pocket. It was quite a thrill. I felt college-aged again, free and unencumbered, as I had not been since my first child was born, more than a quarter of a century before.

It was not until I came back to my much relieved but somewhat disgruntled family, and began to talk about my journey, that I realized how odd it was that I had gone on this trip in the first place. "You went *where?*" friends exclaimed. "But *why?*"

Certainly, the romance of *Lost Horizons*, of visiting the most remote place on earth, played a role in my decision to go. A close friend was making the trip, and I'd have someone I knew well to share the experience with. But I was not, after all, a rock climber or mountaineer or photographer, drawn by the heights and sights of the Himalayas. Trekking was something for younger people, with better knees. And this was no pilgrimage. I was no Buddhist, come to warm my hands at the dying fire of an ancient tradition.

During the weeks after my return, I showed slides to my family and friends, hoping to convey a sense of what it had been like. Even as I extolled the warmth of the Nepalese people, and the austerity and beauty of the Tibetan plateau, I knew I was missing the mark. Exotic as they were, the pictures I'd taken couldn't begin to convey what I'd experienced. All I knew was that there, in that barren, impoverished place, I had felt more alive and more fully myself than at any time in recent memory. For the first time since my diagnosis, I'd felt whole again.

The small group from San Diego with whom I traveled had billed the trip as a "Journey into Self," a description I dismissed at first as just more New Age California jargon. When I met them in Kathmandu, they'd been traveling in India for over a month. There was much talk of various spiritual paths, of kundalini and yin and yang energy. As for me, I kept quiet, certain only that my path, if I had one, was different from theirs.

On our second night, I was introduced to the "Waking Dream," a method of journal-keeping that mines outer experience for personal symbol and meaning. Significant events of the day are examined as symbolic projections of the self, in much the same fashion as the dreams one has during sleep. I'd been exposed before to the "you create your own reality" school of narcissism, which takes this brand of solipsism as literal truth. While not quite ready to accept the notion of "Maya," the world as illusion, I resolved to keep an open mind.

The passage of time since my diagnosis had altered my focus. Yes, I had lost my breast, and yes, I'd had toxic chemicals injected into my body that made me lose my hair, my energy and my appetite. But the medical ordeals of my illness were, for the most part, over now. My immune system appeared to have regained its vitality; I no longer felt sick and tired all the time. The body forgets and forgives. In the end, I was discovering that it was not the physical but the psychic wounds that proved most difficult to heal.

Like my reconstructed breast, or "breast mound" as they referred to it in medical literature, I still often felt like an approximation of my former self. I was less resilient. The scars were fading, but the wide insensate band of flesh across my chest and under my arm still served as a daily reminder. I, too, felt numb at times, a bag of skin with deadened nerves. Covered with clothes, I looked normal. Naked, I didn't. The disparity had widened, the gap between who I was to myself and who I appeared to be, to others—the secret wounds, the public persona.

"You look great!" friends said enthusiastically when they saw me. "Thanks," I'd learned to respond, "I feel fine."

At first, I'd tried giving accurate bulletins to friends who asked, and to some who didn't. But after a few months, my litany of complaints had become tiresome, even to me.

Most people are pragmatic enough to know that, under ordinary circumstances, it's no good to dwell on our misfortunes. Of necessity, we all erect our defenses, depend on our protective filtering to get on with our lives.

But the hardest thing about living with cancer—or perhaps any serious disease whose outcome is uncertain and whose course is unpredictable— is that, over time, it mounts a frontal assault against the very fabric of hope. Perhaps Freud said it most succinctly when he wrote, "Life, as we find it, is too hard." It seems easier, at times, to withdraw into despair and passivity. This is the pessimist's solution: a steady state, negative but predictable, with no nasty surprises.

Before my diagnosis, I'd always thought of myself as an optimist, even something of a stoic. Certainly not a malingerer. But every once in a while, I'd get a glimpse of the way my life had become strung from crisis to crisis. With a shock, I'd realize that I no longer felt secure or safe. That I looked to the future with dread rather than excitement. And I'd think: this can't be happening.

I worried that something was permanently wrong with me, that I'd been damaged or diminished emotionally as well as physically. I couldn't seem to figure out what "getting on with my life" meant, for it seemed as if I wasn't the same person I had been before.

These doubts were insidious; they were always there, gnawing away at any sense of well-being I could muster. Cancer bequeaths a legacy of fear, I was finding, whose only antidote is the passage of time.

But how much time did I have? This new, poignant awareness of time as precious and finite seemed actually to be interfering with my making good use of it. I felt trapped in this irony.

Crisis counselors are fond of telling their clients—or they used to be, back in the 1970s, when this was my profession—that the Chinese calligraph for crisis is a combination of two other symbols: danger and opportunity.

It's more than a cliché, this notion. All pain and loss probably carry some seed of potential within them: a marriage made more intimate, a friendship deepened, a spiritual direction found, a life purpose uncovered, a poem, song, or novel written. We are always reframing.

In *Tales of Power*, the Yaqui sorcerer Don Juan suggests to Carlos Castaneda that the way of the warrior is to live with Death at his left shoulder. A sharpened appreciation of beauty, a tender affection for others, the vivid experience of being alive and of the preciousness of all life, all trivial matters pushed aside for the moment of crisis—these are the gifts that an acquaintanceship with mortality can confer on the living.

But I was no Yaqui warrior. Far from providing liberation, I found the constant awareness of my own possible demise to be paralyzing. Time took on a new sense of imperative. "Are you *really* happy?" a nagging voice within would persist. "Are you *sure* this is what you want to be doing right now?"

"We cannot put off living until we are ready," wrote Jose Ortega y Gasset, the Spanish essayist and philosopher. "The most salient point of life is its coerciveness; it is urgent, here and now without any possible postponement."

For the first time in my life, under the pressure of my disease and the heightened awareness of mortality that accompanied it, I felt a sort of permission—no, an imperative—to pay attention to what was important to me.

I *had* to take care of myself. I had to ask for what I wanted, and not entertain vague expectations that others would anticipate my needs. And later would not do, after everyone else was taken care of: it had to be now, because now might be all there was.

This refocusing on the self, so characteristic of cancer patients—and especially, I would venture to guess, of women who have cancer, because their traditional role as caregivers encourages them in the direction of selflessness, anyway—has often been referred to in the literature as a "benefit" of the illness.

Benefit or not, when treatment is complete and a woman is recovered, at least in the eyes of others, it is all too easy to slip back into the old ways. The crisis appears to be over. Cancer no longer presents itself in its guise of permission-giver and clarifier. The expectations of others renew themselves unchanged, as if the illness had been, for the rest of the family, little more than a difficult interlude, some needed "time off" for Mom.

Deferring pleasures to some distant date no longer seemed wise to me, either, but neither did a heedless insistence on the present moment, to the exclusion of future planning. Another delicate balance, whose fulcrum point is always in flux.

I pestered Tom to take time off from work, so that we could travel together to exotic places we'd never seen. But my timing was lousy. He was involved with his new job. Putting together a treatment center for head injury didn't lend itself to extended vacations. I knew that and I sympathized with his position, yet I felt panicky.

My urgency angered Tom. "Look," he said. "I'm perfectly aware how sick you've been. But it's over, for God's sake. Let's just get back to normal."

"What if I don't have the time to 'get back to normal?' "

He shook his head. "There you go again. Why do you have to keep scaring us silly all the time?"

"I can't seem to get your attention otherwise."

"That's ridiculous," he snapped.

A logical discussion of his work needs always followed, when both of us calmed down. I would have to agree that it made sense for us to continue as we had been, that my nomadic fantasies of our wandering around together like a couple of aging hippies were only that—fantasies. And yet, these feelings of longing kept welling up inside me.

"When will it be my turn?" I'd cry. "What about what I want to do?"

"And just what is it, exactly, that you want to do?"

"I don't know," I would wail.

Eventually, after several of these scenes, we struck a bargain. I agreed to stop using the possibility that my cancer might recur as a bargaining chip in our arguments. He agreed that if I did have a recurrence, he would be willing, if I wanted, to take a leave of absence from work.

Thrust back on my own resources, I plunged back into depression. Just as shuttling from workshop to conference had provided no lasting answers, I knew that travel was really only a distraction. But maybe that was what I needed. At least I could postpone grappling with life at home for another month or two.

And so, chemotherapy and surgeries complete, I planned the trip to Nepal and Tibet. The remoteness of the area drew me; it resonated with my own sense of estrangement. The arduousness of the journey sounded exciting. I'd been living with challenge for more than a year and a half, and was in no mood for a comfortable sojourn in familiar territory. I was looking for something, that was all I really knew. A reward, an escape, an adventure. I didn't know what else to do.

Two weeks before I was scheduled to leave, my mother was hospitalized with pneumonia. By the time I left, she was back at home, on oxygen and, with great reluctance, in the care of a home health care attendant I had hired. I assured everyone concerned that I would call frequently, and that I could be home within a day, if my mother got worse. I purchased travel insurance.

"Are you sure everything's okay?" I asked Tom, when I phoned him from London the day before my plane left for Delhi. By the next night I'd be halfway around the world, and it would be much harder for me to return. If I had to cancel the rest of my trip, I wanted to do it then.

"She wants you to go," Tom told me.

"Yes, but is she all right?"

"She's no worse, from what I can tell. Look, I'll take care of things. You just have a good time."

"Are you really sure?"

"Please," he said in an exasperated tone, and promised to call if there was any serious problem.

Travel in Third World countries means having to come to terms with the disparities of tourist luxury amidst the poverty of daily life. It is not only the difficult living conditions, the steeling of oneself against the sights and smells of the streets, that make such a trip arduous. There is also the feeling of being unwelcome, the resentful stares of the people that provoke shame on the part of the affluent tourist, the begging and desperate maneuvering to offer services for tips, the obsequious pandering of shopkeepers. Despite one's best intentions, it's hard not to retreat into the oasis of the tourist hotel with a sigh of relief. The feeling of insulation, apart from genial tour guides, becomes complete.

But I knew from the moment I landed at the airport in Kathmandu that Nepal would be different—actually, I knew even before that, when I stepped onto the Royal Nepal plane in Delhi. I looked around the airliner with some dismay to see torn upholstery, loose tray tables, a general sense of shabbiness. Quite a change from the spiffy British Airways 747 on which I'd flown from London. Once in the air, however, the smooth whine of engines was reassuring. Despite the charm and doll-like loveliness of the flight attendants, I dared not touch the strange-looking food they offered. I'd been intimidated by the long list of tropical illnesses on the recorded message at the Center for Disease Control. Visions of giardia, dysentery and worse soured my appetite.

By good fortune, I was seated on the left side of the airplane. Before long the Annapurna range of the Himalayas rose like an icy dream on the horizon. I spent the rest of the flight straining for a clear view through my badly scratched window. As we approached Kathmandu, we dipped down below the lush, terraced hills, and the snow peaks disappeared from view. Dirty and scratched as it was, that airplane window could not obscure the beauty that lay beyond it. This seemed the perfect metaphor for Nepal as I experienced it over the next week.

As we wandered in marketplaces and villages and temples in and around Kathmandu, a question began to form in my mind. These people had so little. At forty-seven, I had already far outlived their average life expectancy. The streets were filthy, and evidence of illness and deprivation were everywhere. Yet there was a kind of peace there, a joy in living that was infectious. An inner beauty shone in the faces of the people.

I felt humbled by their sense of presence, by the direct way they met my glance and smiled. I felt welcomed. Loosely translated, their lovely greeting, "Namaste," spoken with hands together and head bowed, means "the soul within me greets the soul within you."

I possessed material comforts beyond their wildest dreams, yet they seemed happier than I was. Was this mere illusion, a traveler's naive perception? Probably. All I knew was that I was moved, as are so many Westerners in Nepal, by the grace and dignity of these people.

At Pashupatinath, the holiest of Shiva temples, I stood on the far bank of the Bagmati River, which flows into the Ganges, watching the kaleidoscope of life unfolding before me. Water buffalo and naked boys swam in water the color of café au lait. People of all ages stood in the river, bathing. Old women picked up the hems of their saris and knelt by the riverside, touching their foreheads with the water. Throngs of pilgrims gathered at the stone *lingams* with offerings of flower petals, red powder, grains of rice. Others descended the steps to fill large brass vessels with the holy water.

The air was perfumed with incense and something more: a smoky, sweetish smell that rose from the burning *ghats* below. Around these cremation platforms, the families of the dead were gathered, but the atmosphere was peaceful, not heavy with mourning as one might expect.

Lost in the scene in front of me, I sat on the stone steps that led down to the water. Existence flows on and on in its myriad variations, I was thinking. Like the river, new life constantly replenishes old, with no separation, no boundaries. Worshiping and bathing take place side by side. People eat, and defecate, and cremate their dead in the most natural way imaginable; children play and mourners weep. The most reverent has its place beside the most mundane. All is accepted and embraced as simply another part of life.

What if I could manage to live this way, I wondered, accepting what had happened in my life without judgment, but with infinite compassion?

Long into that night, I lay in my hotel room, listening to the quiet night sounds of Kathmandu. A stream of vivid images in brilliant colors kept sleep at bay. An endless procession of children's faces, flowers, temple carvings, and all the goods of the marketplace illustrated my eyelids.

I felt so moved by what I'd seen, so connected with it. Why was it I had to come halfway around the world to feel alive again?

My life at home, with its network of obligations and responsibilities, seemed constricted. When I wasn't beset by the expectations of others, my own perfectionistic strivings bound me. But here in Nepal, I was simply being, absorbing. No wonder I felt better. Marvelous as the sights and people of the country were, I understood that it probably wasn't *where* I was, so much as *how* I was, that made the difference. When I finally fell into a fitful doze early that morning, I was no closer to a solution—only, perhaps, a little clearer about the nature of my dilemma.

The next day we were up early and on our way to Pokhara, in central Nepal, in a small, single engine airplane. The Fishtail Lodge, where we were staying, is named for the 26,000-foot peak of Macchapuchare, in the Annapurna range, which looms above it. We had come there to see the mountains, but when we arrived, the high peaks were cloaked in clouds.

After breakfast the following morning, a few of us decided to climb Sarangot, the so-called "Pointed Hill" which stood between us and the snow peaks to the north. As we walked up the well-marked trail from the bazaar in Pokhara, we were joined by several boys, eleven or twelve years old. Two of them, apparently friends, walked with me. Mukti, the quiet one, was tall and slender, with dark shy eyes and a tentative smile. It was he who reached his hand to help me whenever the going became difficult. Sun, whose high cheekbones and slanted eyes gave away his Mongol heritage, chattered merrily and fluently in English, pointing out the sights. I thoroughly enjoyed the companionship of my two young companions, hearing all about their families, school, aspirations.

It was a long and strenuous climb, punctuated by rest stops at small shacks selling soft drinks in glass bottles. In the heat of the day, we walked slowly. Several times we were passed by women carrying huge bundles of firewood, one in particular laboring up the hill with a big woven basket containing what must have been fifty bottles of 7-Up. As the heat gathered its strength, Sarangot began to seem more like a mountain than a hill to me—except, of course, by comparison with the magnificence of the Annapurna range in the distance.

Stopping short of the steep summit, a few of us decided to rest while the others climbed to the top. Our young "guides" conferred among themselves. Sun came forward as their spokesman. They had to leave now, he said to me, and would we please pay them. A little put out by this mercenary turn of events, I gave them what they asked for.

"We shouldn't have given them money, you know," said one of my traveling companions on the way down. "They leave school, I heard, and live off the tourists." I felt upset—naive for believing in the friendship of these boys, and guilty for having contributed to their corruption. All the way down the hill, we were besieged by begging children. It was as if a bulletin had gone out, as perhaps it had.

What had happened with Sun and Mukti continued to disturb me as I wrote in my journal that evening. I reflected unhappily on the role that other "hired friends" had played in my life since my diagnosis. There had been many: therapists, support groups, workshop leaders, doctors, social workers, even masseurs. All of these helpers had served their purpose, but I was tired of being serviced, tired of exchanging money for under-standing and companionship. My illness had estranged me from my real friends.

Back in Kathmandu, we went to the Thamel Market, to equip our-selves for the 600-mile overland journey to Lhasa, the capital of Tibet. I lay awake that night too, anxious and excited.

The thought of being at high altitude, so far from "civilization," scared me. Where we were going, there would be no telephone, no doctors. Tibet's roads were unpaved, the accommodations primitive. It was an oc-cupied country; only a few months earlier, the borders had been closed. There had been recent accounts of civil unrest, eyewitness reports of hundreds of Tibetans shot in Barkhor square in Lhasa the previous March, and stories of tourists expelled for giving out photos of the Dalai Lama to the peasants.

Laden with boots and parkas, dried fruits and chocolate and peanut butter, and several cases of bottled water, we set out early the following morning in Land Rovers. As we approached the Tibetan plateau, the landscape became increasingly wild. Waterfalls hung like veils on the steep hillsides.

At Kodari, on the Nepalese border, a landslide blocked the road. We would have to proceed on foot. Far above us, near the top of the valley, we could see Zhangmu, the Chinese border town where our guide would meet us. Crossing the Friendship Bridge under the watchful eyes of the soldiers, we started up the eleven-kilometer road.

The porters we had hired quickly outstripped us, our suitcases on their backs, taking the steep shortcuts that connected the switchbacks. The young Nepalese boys who had become our self-appointed guides kept trying to convince us to do the same. "This way quick way," they said. "That way very long." At the beginning, we agreed. We scrambled up the first of the shortcuts, being passed by other porters carrying furniture. They put us to shame. Pausing to catch my breath, I saw that one of them, a small wiry fellow with dark skin and high cheekbones, was bent over almost double, carrying a full-length wardrobe on his back, strapped to a tump line across his forehead.

Hours later, in a miserable cold drizzle, we reached Chinese customs. Exhausted, we stood in the rain with our passports and visas as the suspicious agent read our papers, and at last checked into our hotel. Even with no water or heat, and mostly unrecognizable food—one dish appeared to be stir-fried canned peas and Spam—the functional concrete block of a place was far better than we had feared.

The road dust coating the windows of our rickety bus the next morning could not obscure the spectacular landscape as we climbed the rutted switchbacks to the Tibetan plateau. I looked out of my half-open window. Only inches of muddy roadway separated us from a deep chasm. Many hundreds of feet below, the jade river boiled and churned around huge boulders. The bus slipped and slid on the dirt road, which was deeply rutted with mud from the rain the day before. At any moment, a wrong turn of the wheel could send us plunging over the cliff.

Our Tibetan driver and Chinese guide were chatting and laughing. I looked around at my companions; they, too, seemed unconcerned. After a month in India, nothing could faze them. I remonstrated with myself: I was here, there was no turning back. So why not relax and trust that everything would be okay? Anticipating disaster did nothing to avert it, after all.

As I sat back in my seat and let myself calm down, the thought occurred to me that this tendency of mine to worry over things beyond my control applied to more than just a mountainous road in Tibet. For more than a year I'd been living in anxious anticipation of a recurrence of my cancer.

In that moment, I saw clearly how useless this was. Far from buying me protection, this vigilance had soured my life, moment by moment. Even if the worst should happen, this was no way to prepare for it. A far better preparation for disaster was to live as fully and fearlessly as I could, to make the most of my time.

From that moment, I felt no more fear that harm would come to us in Tibet.

As we climbed, the lush bamboo and poplar groves gave way to agave cactus, sedge and twisted dwarf pines that clung tenaciously to the hillside. Farther up, we passed into an alpine region of stunted, low vegetation. Our Chinese guide plucked a tiny white flower and serenaded us with a rendition of "Edelweiss." Sona La, our driver, sang a Tibetan wedding song in a sweet voice: "The white snow flower blossoms on the white snow mountain, and our marriage is like the white snow flower, pure . . . "

On every side were waterfalls that fell a thousand feet or more in long, thin trails of mist, hanging like wisps of cloud against the steep cliff walls. We rose above the treeline and then, at 13,000 feet, emerged onto the barren plateau. The contrast was dramatic; it was as if we had passed into another world.

Panting with the altitude, and trying to ignore a pounding headache, I got out of the bus with the others at La Long La Pass. In a little over two hours, we had climbed from seven thousand feet, in Zhangmu, to nearly seventeen thousand feet.

The faded, shredded prayer flags of a hundred pilgrims adorned the highest point on the road, fluttering like ancient laundry. Among the numerous cairns of stone piled on stone, marking someone's having been there, were interspersed smaller cairns of frozen excrement, sporting little flags of toilet paper.

All around us, the harsh, moonlike desert landscape was utterly barren, all sand and rock in fantastic configurations. A line of snow peaks marched majestically across the southern horizon. Above, the sky was a deep, ringing, cloudless blue, of such intensity that it vibrated against the ocher of the surrounding hills, turning the horizon line into a shining knife's edge of light.

Before reaching Xegar that evening, we were able to see the North Face of Mount Everest, huge and pyramidal despite a distance of some thirty miles. We passed herds of shaggy black yaks. The low mud brick dwellings, with their painted stripes and prayer flags on the four corners, looked much like Native American adobe houses. We'd all heard, of course, of the Siberian-Alaskan land bridge migration theories, but seeing these villages, and the faces of the Tibetan people, so much like those of North American Indians, was evidence of another order.

In the dying light, we stopped at one village to watch the barley harvest. It was hard to believe a life could be scratched out of the barren rock and dust, but we stood there, riveted by the songs of women raising their pitchforks in unison.

The people of the village clustered around us. Although they were curious, they did not at first meet our eyes or smile. Some begged for food, gesturing to their mouths with their fingers. Children and adults alike were so encrusted with dirt that it seemed they must never bathe. Their clothing was ragged, the only adornments being the rough turquoise and coral ear ornaments worn by both men and women. All the children's noses ran. Their straight black hair was slicked down with yak butter, the ubiquitous and rancid-smelling substance that burns in the candles, moistens the skin, and forms the base of *tsampa*, the staple diet of Tibetan peasants, a thick gruel of barley flour and yak butter tea.

At Tashilhunpo Monastery in Xigaze, second only to the Potala Palace in Lhasa in religious significance, brown-robed monks chanted continuously in the temple chamber as they awaited the discovery of the next incarnation of the tenth Panchen Lama. The embalmed body of the Lama, dead only a few months, lay in state behind glass, his eyes wide, a beatific smile on his lips, a gold Rolex on his wrist.

I stood in the dark chamber a long time, listening to the eerie deep chords of the monks' voices, punctuated by drums and bells and the trumpeting blast of conch shells. Hunched over her stick, an aged Tibetan woman hobbled around the room, walking clockwise as all pilgrims must. When she looked up to see the Panchen Lama's face, tears ran down her lined and leathery cheeks. I looked away, moved to tears myself, and then thought of what I'd read about the religious leader, how he had died far away from his people, in Beijing, after years of collaboration with the Communists. How little I understood.

But how little I ever understand of what I see!

A nagging sense of my own encapsulation follows me wherever I travel, particularly when it is so briefly, and on such alien soil. I knew that I could not hope to make sense of the political realities, much less the spiritual realities, that the Tibetan people faced.

I felt a great sadness in Tibet for the decline of a great culture and the loss of its leaders. But perhaps this was more my own sadness, my own sense of loss merely echoed by my surroundings. In the end, I realized, all I could take home, beyond my slides and souvenirs, were my own experiences, which, by definition, said more about me than about anything or anyone else. I flattered myself by thinking that it was modesty, rather than narcissism, to acknowledge this—and perhaps wisdom, or at least good therapy, to make use of the insights gained from this sort of journey.

Trungpa Rimpoche says, "We want to change our lives, rather than use our lives, the present moment." The Buddhist leader is speaking here to his students, about impediments in their spiritual practice, but he might as well be speaking for me, who has no practice I would term "spiritual."

I saw that I hadn't been using my life at all. I'd been running from it, waiting for the crises to ease so that I could get back to "normal," whatever that was.

It was on the long road from Gyantse to Lhasa, on one of several dusty ten-hour days of traveling on bumpy, rutted roads, that I stumbled upon the most profound reasons for coming to Nepal and Tibet.

Bouncing around in the back of the bus with the luggage, scarves tied over our noses and mouths to keep out the dust, one of my fellow travelers and I had been talking about illness and growing older and its impact on our lives. His wife, who was traveling with us as well, had been newly diagnosed with Parkinson's disease.

Thinking of my husband, Tom, back in New York, I was suddenly choked with tears. I missed him acutely at that moment, but then I realized that this was only as it should be. There was a certain necessity to our being apart. It was no accident that I'd come here, beyond the reach of telephones. My journey had been a sort of preparation for both of us, a rehearsal for that final separation from those I loved, for them and for me. Whether those good-byes would come in a year, a decade, or at the end of a long life together, was really beside the point. I needed to be ready, to know I could let go if I had to. The feeling of longing ebbed into a kind of acceptance, like a fist relaxing into an open hand.

I remembered that day a year before when Tom and I had stood by my dying brother-in-law's bed in Ohio. At one point in the late afternoon as the light was fading, Tom and I were alone in the room with Robert and his wife. As Ina rested her head wearily against his shoulder and closed her eyes, Robert, who could no longer speak or open his eyes, moved his arm ever so slightly to embrace her. It was a tender moment, a respite from the grief. Looking at them lying there together so peacefully, I thought, I can do that. If I have to, I can do that.

It was not only the fear of death that had haunted me since my diagnosis, but the fear of the process of dying itself. Everyone knows what a long, drawn-out ordeal a death from cancer can be. I wasn't sure I could handle the indignity, the pain, the loss of function, the terrible leavetaking. The calm and acceptance of that moment in Robert's hospital room was enormously reassuring to me; so, too, was my realization on the bus in Tibet, about leaving the people I loved. That too, I could do if I had to.

That last night, near Gyantse, as I lay in the barley stubble and looked up at the night sky, a shooting star flashed across the Milky Way. I laughed; it was too ideal a conclusion, too perfect a sign. "Did you see that?" I cried, but my two companions hadn't. For a moment, I almost believed I'd made it up.

As I walked back to the hotel, I realized it didn't matter. The outside was inside; it was all one, and I was one with it. I felt privileged to have learned the lessons of this arduous, hostile environment, with its poverty and harsh beauty.

Tom's call didn't come until I was in Bangkok and about to embark on the last leg of my round-the-world trip for a few days' visit to friends in California and Colorado. I had written my mother a postcard every day while I was gone. Most of the cards arrived only after I came home, and several, from Greece, where there was a general strike, never arrived at all.

The telephone startled me from a deep sleep. "I think you better come directly back here," Tom said. "Your mom's not doing so well."

Thanks to the International Date Line and the twelve-hour time change, I was back in New York the very next afternoon—in clock time, but not in real time—after more than twenty-four hours of airports and planes.

By the next morning, I was in Woodstock at my mother's home. I was pleased, but a bit taken aback, by how quickly she seemed to recover in my presence. Within a few hours, her breathing eased. After three days, she felt much better, but I didn't. The feeling of liberation that had accompanied my trip was already beginning to trickle away. Had it all come to this, I wondered? Was I going to let this exhilarating, newfound sense of self I'd discovered half way around the world simply dissolve back into the familiar routine of caretaking?

Two years before, I would have shouldered the yoke of my mother's care without considering any other alternative. I was the daughter, wasn't I? The only and indispensable child who knew her mother's wishes and needs.

Although my mother was loath to accept help from others, I forced the issue by carrying on with my own life. While I still cooked and froze most of her evening meals—a ritual she found so comforting I hadn't the heart to refuse—I arranged for others to shop, run errands, act as chauffeur, and carry out all the small tasks I had assumed as my responsibility since my father's death, eleven years before. I cut down my visits to one or two days a week.

Of course, some part of me still cringed at the thought of putting myself first—especially when she was ill and I was about to embark on something as frivolous as a vacation.

But I made myself do it anyway.

My trip had shown me what was possible. It wasn't about going around the world; that much was clear. To retain the spirit of that journey, I'd have to map out a new itinerary, one more difficult and demanding, day by day.

This time, I would find what I needed much closer to home.

NINE

The Waiting Room

I said to my soul, be still, and wait without hope
For hope would be hope for the wrong thing
— T.S. ELIOT,
"East Coker"

I T WAS SIX months after my trip, a little over two years since my diagnosis. I approached the familiar door on Fifth Avenue with my head down, as though I were diving into cold water. I even held my breath. Oblivious to the evidence of construction and the hand-written sign that instructed me to use the lobby entrance on 96th Street, I pressed the bell and waited for the buzzer to let me in. Nothing.

After ringing again, twice, and picking my way through the plaster rubble in the anteroom, I was let into the office.

"Can't you read?" the receptionist said with irritation. "Didn't you see the sign?"

Not hello. Not how are you feeling and, gee, you look great. I mumbled something about being sorry, and turned to the coatrack. Already, I could feel the tears coming.

I knew that I was overreacting to the receptionist's crankiness. For several days, approaching this quarterly checkup, I'd been on edge. It was my own form of PMS—Premedical Syndrome. This particular round of appointments had been complicated by a mammogram the week before and a disquieting chat with the radiologist about the micro-calcifications she had found in my remaining breast, which might or might not turn out to be the beginnings of a new cancer.

I was primed for upset, ready to be thrust back into the morass of raw emotions in which I wallowed for so long after my diagnosis. While I knew first-hand that illness can regress perfectly mature adults, turning them into whiny, tantrum-throwing toddlers, it still stunned me how small and forlorn I could feel, and with what little provocation.

So many times during the two years following my diagnosis I found myself dissolved in tears at a store counter or on the street. Of necessity, I had learned to take this sulky child inside me in firm control, to sit her down and make her behave. Dry your eyes, I would tell her. The receptionist is just having a bad day; don't take it so personally. Never mind that she seemed like a friend a year ago. She's busy now; look how full the waiting room is. And think of what it's like for her to greet cancer patients day in and day out, the depression settling everywhere like the plaster dust.

Being there again, it all came back to me. The months of treatments mixed with the particular yet indescribable smell of the place, sour and medicinal, the hodgepodge of tasteless decorations, the coatrack standing in the corner like a bedraggled scarecrow.

Often during my treatment, I would bolster my flagging spirits with what one text on psychological adjustment to illness calls "comparison with less fortunate others." However nauseated I felt, there was always someone greener than I was. However thin my hair became, there was someone else who had lost all of hers. However anxiety-ridden I was about what lay ahead, there was someone whose illness had obviously advanced beyond mine. "It could be worse," I told myself, clinging to my protective frame of reference. For a time, this was my amulet, to be taken out a dozen times a day.

All that was over, thank God. A year and a half had elapsed since the end of the chemotherapy. I didn't look sick anymore. My hair was thick again and curlier than it had been before, but it had also become coarse and much grayer. I had most of my energy back; never mind that my white blood count was below what it used to be, and that I was still having hot flashes. Anti-inflammatory medication kept the joint pain brought on by my chemotherapy-induced menopause at a bearable level. In any way that could be objectively measured, I was recovered.

A majority of recurrences of breast cancer, I'd read, take place within two years of the end of treatment. This should have made me feel more secure, since I was almost at that point. But such information only made me uneasy. If I took it to heart, it could easily turn on me, and make me look up the charts of what the statisticians call "disease-free survival" in my textbook on breast cancer. This was never a good idea, since the numbers there were so dismal. It could make me press my oncologist to talk about percentages and odds, something he hated to do, for he knew as little as I did about my longterm prognosis. All he could tell me was that sixty to ninety percent of women like myself—that is, same kind and stage of cancer, same treatment—show no evidence of disease five years after diagnosis.

I didn't find even the higher figure reassuring, however, since I—like every woman with the disease—had lost that nine-to-one gamble once already, and could never comfortably hide in the majority again.

There were other statistics that haunted me, too, numbers that transcended the merely personal. Not long ago, a group of militant lesbian women, imitating the gay activist group Act-Up, erected a billboard on a prominent street in San Francisco that read: "Thirty women dead from breast cancer every hour. Marked for death by the National Cancer Institute."

While the numbers they used were inflated—in fact, five women die of breast cancer every hour—I, too, felt a sense of outrage. I was angry that more resources have not been allocated to this leading killer of women in middle age. I was angry that many women still didn't know the most basic facts about breast cancer. I was angry that poor and minority women receive inferior screening and treatment and die in disproportionate numbers. I was angry that mammography, much touted as the ultimate in "early detection," is helpful for only thirty percent of women with breast cancer—even when it is properly utilized. I was angry that the National Cancer Institute has dragged its heels on funding research on possible environmental and dietary factors contributing to this growing epidemic. I was angry that the causes of breast cancer are still unknown, with seventy to eighty percent of women diagnosed having no known risk factors whatsoever.

In the civil rights climate of the late 1960s and early 1970s, it was the tactics and political effectiveness of the women's movement that inspired the gay liberation movement to take action against discrimination. Now, ironically, the chain of influence had come full circle, and it was the success of AIDS activists in marshaling research money, and gaining access to experimental drug trials, that was inspiring women with breast cancer to unite and begin to press for more funding and research for our disease.

By 1991, government spending for AIDS research was at a level almost nineteen times that for breast cancer, which represented only a little more than one percent of the NIH budget. This was true despite the fact that in just the previous year more American women had been diagnosed with breast cancer than all the reported cases of AIDS in this country since the start of the epidemic. This despite the fact that there had been four times as many breast cancer deaths as AIDS deaths since 1980.

Yet I could hardly begrudge the success of AIDS activists; I admired it. Clearly, it could serve as a model and an inspiration for women with breast cancer.

Survivorship can be an isolating business. If they are able, most women prefer to forget that breast cancer has ever happened to them, and sink back gratefully into the normalcy of the healthy world. A disease that proves fatal to a minority of its victims is bound to be less unifying than one that kills or visibly disables all who have it.

Advocacy and political action, by contrast, is often fueled by a continuing sense of personal engagement and the imperative of ongoing treatment needs. For those who are fatally ill—with AIDS, for example—activism can become a way both of channeling a sense of outrage at an inevitable end, and of dignifying an otherwise meaningless loss.

Until quite recently, having had breast cancer was—for most women—if not an occasion for shame, then at least not a subject to be discussed in polite society. The fact that many public figures have "come out of the closet" has changed this, at least to some extent.

Still, as Audre Lorde points out, the norms of society dictate that women who have had breast cancer further conceal that fact from one another and from the world by means of prosthesis and reconstructive surgery. "Women with mastectomies must become visible to each other," she insists. "For silence and invisibility go hand in hand with powerlessness."

Differences in treatment and prognosis further separate afflicted women. Befriending women with breast cancer involves taking some emotional risks. Over time, there will be losses. As evidence that women with breast cancer are by and large loath to gather together and are not encouraged to do so by the predominantly male medical community, one has only to look at the relative scarcity of support groups such as the one I joined, despite the growing experimental evidence that such support can prolong life dramatically in women with metastatic cancer.

Cancer is, both subjectively and symbolically, a personal and individual experience. The body is at war with itself. The war is invisible, and therefore consummately private.

Invisibility, isolation, and uncertainty are hallmarks of this disease. Women with breast cancer must live with uncertainty every day. It is this that makes them struggle to forget and repress what has happened, and to avoid contact with other women with breast cancer. It is this that creates ambivalence about advocacy and political involvement.

And it was this uncertainty that was sending me back to see my doctors every three months with moist palms and a pounding heart, ready to weep at the slightest provocation, rather than feeling like a proud and victorious veteran of some mortal struggle. My problem was, I didn't know if the war was over.

I'd lost more than a breast to this illness. Sitting in that waiting room, I was aware that I had left something else of myself there in this functional gray space, among the unclaimed umbrellas and tattered magazines.

Illness is a wedge driven between us and our illusions, it seems to me now, a widening rift through which we are forced to glimpse the depth of our fears, the limitations of our mortality. It's as if there is another immune system inside each of us, a non-physical protective filter between the harshness of reality and the tenderness and brevity of our lives. Like white blood cells engulfing bacteria, our fantasies and illusions attack the ugly facts of existence, smoothing the jagged edges and blunting their capacity to hurt.

Without these defenses, the wounds are too raw; the spirit despairs and becomes bitter. Yet the healing of this fragile tissue of hope and optimism is painfully slow, and it is easily ripped asunder by any new insult.

Sitting in that waiting room, I was nurturing that new skin carefully, shielding it from further assaults.

Pretending a cold, I wiped my nose and took a quick survey of the other patients. As always when I was there, I found myself wondering who was in treatment, who in remission.

All during my chemotherapy, I would see the same people coming in for their injections, week after week. There was the terribly thin man whose skin was a pallid yellow gray, whose daughter sat anxiously on the edge of her seat the whole time they were there, her eyes darting everywhere in the room, while her father folded his emaciated frame into the chair and leaned back to close his eyes, exhausted. The chatty, plump matron with the Hungarian accent and the blond wig that always seemed askew, who knitted formless hats and socks unceasingly. The somber, middle-aged black couple who waited patiently, hands folded, never exchanging a word or a glance. We never spoke, never shared our stories, these people and I, though we would nod and smile the tired smile of the initiated, if our eyes happened to meet.

There were new people in the waiting room, patients whom I didn't recognize. I saw the same look in their eyes, a look of apprehension, resignation, and that deep weariness the chemicals bring. I sensed the same kinship with these strangers that I had felt with those who had been my fellow travelers when I was in treatment. I wanted to tell them how good it was to enjoy food again, to not have that bitter, metallic taste in my mouth, how wonderful to awaken refreshed, to not always feel as if one is wearing, as my friend Miriam described it, "a pile of dirty overcoats." That sense of being toxic, poisoned, dissipates in time, I wanted to reassure them. They would end, these interminable treatments.

I felt a twinge of pride for having stayed the course. Still, the fear was always there that I might find myself sitting here again, waiting for the injections that would send me home sick and exhausted.

A woman younger than I, leaned painfully on her cane, shuffling in small steps. Her face was framed by a cap of dark brown artificial curls, in sharp contrast with the pallor of her skin. Had it gone to her bones, I wondered, or was her faltering gait some side effect of the treatment?

Did we share the same illness, she and I? Was she me, six months from now, or a year, or five years? I didn't even know if I should be using the present tense, or the past, when I talked about my illness. I didn't know whether to say I *have* cancer, or I've *had* cancer.

For the most part, it was past tense I found myself using. The risk had been blunted somewhat by the passage of time. Each day with no symptoms provided new evidence. The weight of the entire experience was gradually being overbalanced by the days and months of relative health and well-being since the end of my treatment. It was a subtle but profound shift, and one for which I was grateful daily.

I felt healthy enough. I looked fine. But this was no real measure, I realized. I had believed once that it was, but I'd learned the hard way that one does not grasp these things intuitively. At the time of my diagnosis, I'd felt just fine, too, blithely convinced even during the biopsy that this persistent lump in my right breast was merely another cyst. But this is another hallmark of cancer in its early stages: except for the treatment, patients feel deceptively normal.

So what sense was I to make of this new state of innocence now, after all that had happened? It was hard to know whether to cultivate these illusions again, as an antidote to anxiety-ridden vigilance. On good days, I almost believed that I was cured. On bad days, I worried that this new optimism was only a sign of my own dumb gullibility, not to be trusted.

Like the daughter of that man in the waiting room, I was still perched on the literal and figurative edge of my seat, preparing for bad news or for something else to happen. There would be no more nasty surprises, I vowed.

But there is no such thing as preparation for devastating news; it is always a shock. Being able to say, "I knew it all the time," is no comfort at all.

The waiting room had emptied. At last, it was my turn.

The technician called me in and stuck my finger. The drop of blood was analyzed. "Wait a minute," she said, as I rose from the chair. "Don't you want the report?" I shook my head. Each time before, I had asked for the computer printout of my blood analysis, carefully logging my white blood count from visit to visit. It was time to let go of that anxious little habit, too—time to stop worrying about my immune system.

Pleased with myself, I went back out to the waiting room and sat down, holding a gauze square to my finger. In another minute, my name was called. The nurse who administered all of my chemotherapy was standing in the hallway, holding my file, and I realized how genuinely pleased I was to see her, how grateful I had always been for her gentleness and precision. I told her so, and she patted my arm. "It's good you feel that way," she said, laughing. "We had a patient once—every time he saw me, he threw up. Before I even touched a needle!"

As I passed her desk on my way to the examining room, the receptionist looked up and smiled broadly at me, the earlier episode forgotten. "So, how are you?" she asked. "You look terrific."

During the summer of 1990, Miriam—the woman in the group with whom I'd maintained the closest ties—felt a swelling beneath her ribs. Her oncologist sent her home, reassuring her it was nothing to worry about; he hadn't found anything amiss. Two months later, when the swelling had grown, she made another appointment to see him. Again, he dismissed her symptoms. Still alarmed, she went to another doctor, who immediately ordered a CAT scan, which revealed that she had three large, actively-growing tumors in the internal mammary lymph nodes under the ribs on the affected side, near her heart and lungs.

An aggressive course of radiation followed, accompanied by a painful bout of shingles, lung irritation and cough from the radiation that persisted for months and made ominous shadows on a bone scan. The tumors disappeared.

She and her husband Gary took a trip to the Caribbean, to lie in the sun and do, as she put it, "absolutely nothing."

"They're not talking cure anymore," Miriam told me when she returned. "Management is the new word." Her new oncologist—"Not a nice guy, but then I wasn't looking for nice this time. Look what happened with an oncologist that I liked!"—encouraged her to sign up for a research study of Taxol, an experimental drug made from the bark of the Pacific Yew tree, and to consider having an autologous bone marrow transplant (ABMT), a potentially risky process that involved administration of extremely high-dose chemotherapy.

These same treatment options were offered to Pat, whose breast cancer had also metastasized that fall, shortly after her marriage. After trying to ignore a persistent ache in her hip for some weeks, she had gone to see her oncologist. Scans and a biopsy revealed a malignant tumor in the pelvic bone near her hip socket.

At our group meeting the week before all this had happened, we had been comparing our lower back pain, sore knees and other assorted aches, our anxieties clearly magnified by Miriam's recurrence. And now Pat was, as Miriam said, "in the soup again, too."

After the shock of that discovery and the frantic searching for information that ensued, Pat was at last able to sleep once again, she told the group at our next meeting. She and her doctors had mapped out a strategy. With the Taxol—considered by some the most promising cytotoxic drug in many years—and a bone marrow transplant to follow once the Taxol had reduced the hip tumor, she felt there was still hope.

"Someone's got to survive," she told us. "Why shouldn't it be me?" Still in her thirties, she was young and strong; she intended to fight her disease in the most aggressive way possible.

Miriam wasn't keen on heroic measures, she confided to me. She knew there would be other recurrences. But during the good time that remained, she wanted to focus on Gary, their dogs and the house in the country. "One of these times, they won't be able to treat it anymore," she said matter-of-factly. "I'll just have to face that when it comes."

After her radiation treatments were over, Miriam had chosen a wait-and-see approach, with the new oncologist monitoring her progress every few weeks. One of her two dogs, a mastiff, died, which was a real blow for Miriam. After much deliberation, as an expression of faith in the future, she and her husband bought a mastiff puppy they called Tigerlily.

By the following spring, however, fearful that the rest of the slots in the experimental protocol would be taken, Miriam had joined the Taxol study. Three new shadows, two in her liver and one on her vena cava, all inaccessible to biopsy but clearly visualized in the CAT scan, persuaded her. Less than a year after the radiation, the cancer was back.

When I visited Pat and Miriam on the twelfth floor of the hospital where they came for their treatments every three weeks, I found them together, although they hadn't been assigned to the same room. For each treatment, they were connected to a portable pump for a twenty-four hour continuous infusion, through a device called a Portocath. When the superficial veins of the arms and hands have been damaged by adjuvant chemotherapy, the administration of new intravenous drugs is often done through a port surgically implanted beneath the skin in one of the large veins in the chest. This also simplifies the process of drawing blood, which can become a time-consuming ordeal for everyone.

Their hair had gone quickly, this time. Both of them wore headscarves for comfort; for the moment, wigs and prostheses were stashed in closets, or drawers. No need for pretense in that setting.

That day, they were cheerful, conspiratorial, gossiping in whispers about their roommates. One, a young girl, listened incessantly to loud music and was nasty to her parents. Another, an older lady with a pronounced Eastern European accent, had been dealing with recurrences of her breast cancer for twelve years with hormonal therapy, all the while rejecting the usual cytotoxic agents. "They are not natural," this woman insisted, as if the powerful hormones that had caused her to grow a beard and mustache, and to gain fifty pounds, had been. Taxol was made from trees, she told Pat. That made it all right. Pat suppressed a desire to ask the woman if she knew that Native American tribes had used it to poison their arrows.

I sat there, mostly quiet, listening to their talk of treatment delays, lost records, and the endless waiting of hospital routine. They spoke of the days of exhaustion and malaise after the treatments, the bone pain from self-injected recombinant granulocyte stimulating factor (GCSF), which kept their white blood counts at an acceptable level, and of the extensive recordkeeping and blood tests that an experimental trial entailed.

"I don't feel the same sense of dread this time around," Pat said. "It's easier, somehow, familiar. I know how to do this, I guess."

For Eva, the bad news came in a telephone call from her oncologist. One of the routine blood-screening tests for cancer had come back with elevated levels. A liver scan revealed two small spots. Since an MRI and CAT scan shed no further light, a biopsy was performed. "They said it wouldn't be bad," she told me, "but I felt violated. And it hurt like hell." Thankfully, the biopsy was negative. What were the spots? Probably small blood vessels, she was told.

Now Eva could go back to figuring out what to do about her polyurethane-coated breast implant. Recent information had been released about the potentially carcinogenic byproducts produced by the foam coating. Her first impulse had been to have it removed immediately, but a Canadian plastic surgeon, an expert in the problems associated with these particular implants, warned her that early removal might result in intractable infection from the partially decomposed polyurethane foam. It was better to wait at least eight to ten months, he told her.

Ronnie, one of the two women in our group who'd chosen lumpecto-my plus radiation, rather than mastectomy, continued to worry about a hard nodule that had appeared near where her cancer had been before. Her surgeon was reluctant to operate unless it was absolutely necessary. After radiation treatment, a simple biopsy was no longer so simple, it turned out. Irradiated tissue might not heal easily, and could become in-fected. "But they don't tell you that, when you make your choice for treatment," she said. "I mean, I knew that if the cancer came back, if I ever had to have a mastectomy, reconstructive surgery might be a prob-lem, but not this." For now, they were watching the nodule, to see if it changed.

Led by a social worker, our weekly breast cancer support group had originally been based in the cancer rehabilitation service of the hospital where I'd had my mastectomy. While I was in Nepal and Tibet during the fall of 1990, the hospital had closed the service and ended our meet-ings. Because we all felt strongly about remaining in contact with one another, we began gathering every three months for a potluck supper and a "leaderless" meeting.

Although we invited Barbara each time, she hadn't come, and hadn't contacted anyone in the group about it. Finally, one of the group mem-bers called her and found out that she, too, was struggling with a recurrence.

"I didn't want to bring everybody down," she offered, by way of expla-nation.

In truth, our meetings were often sobering. With two members of the group having recurrences so far, and various scares occurring with some regularity for others, we were balanced precariously between reassur-ance and alarm as we shared our stories. The solace of identification and the fear provoked by that identification rubbed shoulders all the time.

After we had eaten all the healthy, low-fat food we virtuously brought to share with one another, the nine of us would settle down to go around the circle, getting reports from each woman.

Having betrayed us once, our bodies were difficult to read. Each new symptom we experienced contained a seed of self-doubt. If we paid at-tention to it, were we being alarmist? If we didn't, were we in denial? Ordinary signs of aging, lower back pain and stiff joints, became magnified. Any slight thickening or swelling in the remaining, precious breast terrified us.

Those dealing with recurrences formed a sort of vanguard, serving as scouts for the difficult terrain ahead that the rest of us might yet have to cross. I listened to their stories with conflicting emotions: I wanted to hear, and yet I didn't want to hear. Knowing the concrete details and decisions about treatments that my friends were facing made that future somehow less scary. But it also made it seem more real, more possible. Driven by my own anxiety, I found myself almost as hungry for first-hand knowledge as when I was first diagnosed. I could see that Miriam and Pat were coping somehow, and that gave me faith that I would find the means, too, if I had to.

The younger women, not yet in menopause, spoke wistfully of child-bearing. For those who had never had children, the poignancy of late-in-life deadlines was sharpened to a fine edge by the threat of cancer returning. There was the possibility that the hormonal storms of pregnancy might, in some cases, provoke a recurrence. "Is it a selfish thing to want a child when you can't be sure you'll be around to raise it?" one woman asked. Her gynecologist had told her, in no uncertain terms, that it was.

As time went by, I could see that we, who had felt such unity in the face of our shared illness, were becoming divided by our differing prognoses. Of course I was grateful to be a member—so far—of the larger group that was apparently disease-free, yet I felt uneasy, too. Why them and not me, I wondered.

Our lives were measured out in three-month increments. It took a while for me to realize that we had scheduled these group get-togethers every quarter, in an unconscious echo of our checkup schedules.

"Your hemoglobin's a little low," my oncologist said as he began to examine me on my next visit. "Nothing to be alarmed about, though."

Opening the skimpy gown, I showed him the new incision on my reconstructed breast, which was still bloated and taut with serum and blood from the surgery less than two weeks before, where the all-saline implant had replaced the one that contained silicone gel.

"I'm sure that explains it, then." He felt for enlarged lymph nodes in my neck. "Why'd you have it done? It looked fine to me as it was."

"I didn't want silicone in my body," I told him. "I figure I have enough to worry about."

He raised his eyebrows. "Take a deep breath, please," he said, fitting his stethoscope to my back. "And now, another."

Of the doctors I'd consulted about this surgery, only one, my brother-in-law, encouraged me to do it, or even understood why it was that I felt the exchange of implants was important. After all, didn't millions of women have silicone gel implants? As one plastic surgeon said to me, "Don't you think we'd know about it if there were problems?"

They'd all thought the procedure completely unnecessary, and told me I was overreacting. Yet I'd been sure it was the right thing to do. For once, I paid attention to that feeling. Every time I picked up the *Times* and read one more story about the FDA threatening to take silicone implants off the market unless they were proven safe, I rejoiced in those instincts. It was something recent, I realized, this new self-trust, combined as it was with a healthy skepticism about the infallibility of medicine.

"Don't think of yourself as having cancer," my oncologist advised, when I was dressed again and sitting in his office. "You're fine. It's in the past."

"Yes," I said, meaning no, I can't think that way, not yet, and especially not here. "But how long, really, before I can be reasonably sure it won't recur?"

"Five years."

"But I thought most breast cancers recurred in the first two years after treatment."

"The more serious cancers show up sooner."

"So you're saying it could come back at any time."

"Look," he said, leaning forward. "What good does it do you to think that way? You have to go on with your life."

We were silent for a moment. I gazed at the wooden sailboats on his desk, at the stack of patient charts awaiting his attention, the sagging bookshelf that always looked as if all the heavy tomes on oncology were about to come crashing down.

"How would I be able to tell if something's wrong?" I asked. "I mean, what kind of thing should I be looking for?"

He gave me an exasperated smile. "I'll say it again: I don't want you to be looking for anything."

"You don't want me to be vigilant."

"That's exactly right."

I felt defensive. "I'm not this anxious all the time, you know. You just see me that way because that's how I feel, coming here to see you every three months."

"Then we'll make it four months this time. Look, I have an idea: how about if you thought of me as your internist, not your cancer doctor?"

"Oh, come on," I replied incredulously. "You don't want to hear all my other little complaints, do you?"

"Sure, why not?"

But even as he said this, I knew that I would not consult him for minor ailments, that what he was suggesting was only a trick of the mind, a way of coping with these checkups and the reminders of illness and foreboding they created.

Across time and distance, the memory of that wild bus ride in remote Tibet flashed once more through my mind. It was again time to let go, to trust. One of those essential lessons that must be relearned, over and over.

The oncologist got up, reached across his desk for my hand with a smile. "And no more surgery. Okay?"

"Right," I said. "No more surgery."

Feeling released, reprieved, I slipped out of the office, past a room full of depressed-looking patients waiting for their chemotherapy treatments, into the summer sunlight and green of Central Park across the street.

TEN

An Inconspicuous Marvel

The future is like the daytime moon, a diffident but
faithful companion, so elegant as to be almost invisi-
ble, an inconspicuous marvel.
— ROBERT GRUDIN,
*Time and the Art of
Living*

PERUSING THE OBITUARY page every day, as is my morbid habit,
I find myself searching out the premature deaths of the well-
known and accomplished people who have been allotted a para-
graph or two, sometimes even a column, in the newspaper. I look for
the ones who have died young, in their forties and fifties and sixties, and
for the name of the disease that has brought about these untimely deaths.
AIDS heads that list, of course, then various forms of cancer, and heart
attacks.

On the *New York Times* obit page, women are a decided minority.
More of my sex die unremarked and uncelebrated than men do, a sad
and final chauvinism. Still, we are represented.

Whenever the cause of death is listed as breast cancer, my heart sinks.
Of course I know perfectly well that tens of thousands of American
women will die of the disease this year, but reading about one life lost
at a time is different, more real.

The fourth year since my diagnosis has been a time of loss. Last March
my mother died peacefully, at eighty-three, of congestive heart failure.
Tom and I were with her at the end. In April, we celebrated her life and

her poetry with friends. After all my complaints, I found I missed taking care of her. The days each week that I would drive to Woodstock to see her seemed empty, although the house was, and still is, full of her presence. Not a day goes by that I don't have the impulse to pick up the telephone to call her, to share some bit of news, to find out how she's doing.

A few months after my mother's death, her sister, my Aunt Jo, passed away in the nursing home where she had been confined since her stroke. Then, with the deaths last autumn of my first husband's mother and father, my sons had lost their remaining three grandparents in half a year. The sense of a generation passing was inescapable.

A somber year, a sad year. But these deaths were all timely, at the end of full lives. Such was not the case for Miriam.

Witnessing the slow misery of a cancer death is, sadly, a common experience. For the members of our support group, being present during Miriam's last months was particularly hard. We were losing a friend we loved, to a disease that all of us shared. Seeing her, being with her, our own fears for ourselves assumed frighteningly real dimensions. Death in the abstract was replaced by visible decline and suffering.

As the fall of 1992 progressed, movement became more and more difficult for Miriam. In September, she could still walk slowly, with a cane; by November, she was confined to her bed, her bones riddled with disease.

Toward the end, avoiding pain became a central concern. One day, I walked into her hospital room to find Miriam, usually the picture of stoicism, sobbing. At the sight of me, she drew the sheet up over her face in embarrassment. Wiping her eyes, she apologized for her tears, and told me what had happened. Returning from X-ray, she'd been left sitting in a wheelchair for an interminable time before the nurses had come to put her in bed. By this time, standing, sitting—any change in position—had become excruciating.

One night a week or so later, the simple act of rolling over in bed led to a fractured shoulder and upper arm. A surgery to pin the break was followed by others to sever nerves and relieve pain.

Through all of this, Miriam's spirit continued, indomitable, uncomplaining, and full of surprising wit. I found myself drawn to her bedside, to her impressive equanimity, never quite sure whether I was taking or giving comfort there. Drugged, immobilized, she still wanted to know about the world outside, what we thought, how we felt. Over cartons of take-out Chinese food, we came to know Miriam's husband, Gary, and her other friends.

On the last day she was able to choose pain-ridden consciousness over morphine-mediated oblivion, Miriam asked one of her oldest friends if she, Miriam, should say hello to the friend's mother, who had died not long before.

"Do you suppose . . . ?" the friend mused out loud later to me as we stood in the hallway outside the hospital room; then, answering her own question, shaking her head: "Nah, she's never believed in that kind of thing. She must have been pulling my leg."

It made me think of my mother. She, too, had never believed in "that kind of thing."

"I'm leaving soon," my mother had told a member of the family a day or two before she died.

"You mean you're going home?" he asked, taken aback.

"No, there," she replied, pointing up. "I'm going there."

A semi-credulous agnostic myself, I found it reassuring to know that Miriam, like my mother, had entertained the possibility of an afterlife, and found comfort, or at least humor, there.

Then, all at once, the whispered hallway conferences, late-night telephone calls, the urgency of saying our good-byes was all past. In early December, the vigil was over.

When our group met again, after Christmas, we spoke of helplessness and loss. We shared our fears, our anger. Out of the grief came a decision to work together for changes in funding, research and services for women with breast cancer. As a group, calling ourselves "Tigerlily" after Miriam's beloved mastiff, we joined the National Breast Cancer Coalition, a new lobbying and advocacy organization based in Washington, whose work in the past year has helped to more than double federal appropriations for breast cancer research in 1993. Thanks to their efforts, a Mammography Quality Standards Act has been passed by Congress, as well as a Cancer Registries Act, which has yet to gain funding.

With Miriam's death, I began reading again, avidly following the various developing news stories relating to breast cancer. The past two years had brought a number of changes, I discovered.

Two studies in Canada and Sweden, together involving some 85,000 women, failed to discover any improvement in mortality rates with screening mammography for women in their forties in the first five to seven years of follow-up.

While it is possible that faster-growing, more aggressive tumors in younger women might be a cause, it is likely that mammograms simply don't pick up tumors in this premenopausal age group, whose breast tissue is often dense and cystic. This finding disputed previous wisdom that mammography was equally effective for pre- and postmenopausal women, which had led to the recommendation a decade ago that women in their forties have regular mammograms.

It was these NCI guidelines, in fact, that have led more than a third of American women under fifty to have the screening—a far larger percentage, ironically, than women *over* fifty, who derive clear and undisputed benefits from the test. Only a fifth of women in their sixties and seventies, at highest risk for breast cancer, have regular mammograms. Perhaps if the pictures women saw in magazines urging breast self-examination and mammography didn't use such young, attractive models, older women might identify and get the message.

The research findings came as no surprise to those of us in my support group, myself included, whose false-negative mammograms had contributed to delay in our diagnoses. While experts worry about recommendations, women under fifty must again take the decision-making power back for themselves. If, in talking with their radiologists, they discover that their mammograms are indeed uninformative, an extra measure of vigilance in breast self-examination is called for.

Despite the scary lifetime incidence figures, women with no high-risk factors should realize that, according to the National Cancer Institute Surveillance Program, by age forty, only one woman in 217 will have been diagnosed with breast cancer. By age forty-five, it is one woman in ninety-three; by age fifty, one woman in fifty. The oft-quoted one-in-eight or one-in-nine incidence figure expresses cumulative risk over an entire lifetime.

Perhaps because I've met so many women myself in this category, it surprised me to discover that only twenty-two percent of women diagnosed with breast cancer each year are under the age of fifty. These figures must not, however, mask the disproportionate increase in high-risk, more lethal breast cancers in younger women in this country, growing at a rate higher than anywhere else on earth.

The reasons for this are still unknown. So-called "lifestyle factors," such as high-fat diet, obesity, late pregnancies, lack of exercise, and alcohol consumption have all been implicated. A recent public hearing in New York, sponsored by an advocacy group from Nassau County, which has the highest breast cancer incidence in the United States, addressed the role of environmental factors, a largely-neglected area of research. A growing body of scientific evidence suggests a link between increased breast cancer and environmental contaminants such as PCBs, DDT and other carcinogenic pesticides, toxic waste sites, sources of ionizing radiation, and electromagnetic fields.

Breast cancer incidence has been on the rise in recent years, particularly in the last decade. In 1972, lifetime incidence was only one in fourteen. Some officials attribute the thirty percent increase in overall incidence of breast cancer in the United States since 1982 to the increase in screening mammography picking up earlier, smaller and non-palpable tumors in the population—not "new" cancers, but newly-detected cancers found years before they would have been otherwise. They believe that incidence will now steadily decrease to 1980 levels. "It's inappropriate to say there's an epidemic," says Dr. Larry Kessler, of the National Cancer Institute, who prefers the word "endemic," meaning constantly present. "As populations grow and women live to old age, it (breast cancer) is just around . . . We don't need to make women afraid."

Epidemic or not, no one can dispute the fact that at least 1.6 million American women alive today have been diagnosed with breast cancer. Another one million don't even know they have it yet. The National Cancer Institute projects 182,000 new cases in 1993, and forty-six thousand deaths. Breast cancer remains the most common form of cancer in women, and is the leading cause of death in women between the ages of thirty-two and fifty-two.

It is a good sign that breast cancer has at last become a highly-politicized issue, drawing heated public debate. At last, we're on the national agenda. The reality is, we live in a crisis-oriented society. The most frightening figures and the loudest voices will get the research dollars.

At the 1992 FDA hearings on silicone gel breast implants, emotional pleas were heard from both sides. Plastic surgeons gathered testimonials from satisfied patients. Women spoke passionately of the crucial importance of implants to their sense of psychological well-being. Others, equally passionate, told horror stories of ruptures and crippling arthritis, lupus and scleroderma. It was clear that some women feared what other women advocated: that the implants would be removed altogether from the marketplace.

Following a three-month moratorium, the FDA announced in April 1992 that it would permit restricted use of silicone gel implants in women with breast cancer and traumatic injury enrolled in federally-controlled safety studies. The hundreds of studies previously supplied by implant manufacturers were deemed insufficient to prove the safety of these devices.

The growing number of reports of women with systemic side effects is undeniable, but no direct causal relationship has yet been established. Some make the claim that implants interfere with mammography, a crucial issue for the million or so American women with breast augmentation. As time goes on, more complaints about capsular contracture, infections, and rupture or leakage are being reported.

Meanwhile, the FDA, concerned about the climate of fear provoked by these reports, advises women with silicone gel implants for augmentation or reconstruction, who are not symptomatic, to do nothing.

I find this advice puzzling. To let well enough alone, a woman has to be willing to bank on the complete safety of the implants, which has yet to be proven. Once spread through the lymphatic system, the gel from a ruptured implant cannot be removed. No one really knows how silicone gel reacts with the human body; if it is harmless, as a majority of plastic surgeons claim, or if it causes autoimmune disorders and, perhaps, some forms of cancer. No hard data exists yet about implants interfering with mammograms. Like so much else in breast cancer treatment, there are no clear answers. Each woman must decide for herself.

Meanwhile, hundreds of cases are now in litigation. Despite the lack of causal proof, several lawsuits have so far resulted in multimillion-dollar settlements.

The potential risks of the polyurethane foam coating and the silicone gel inside her implant had left Eva wishing she had never considered reconstruction in the first place. With the help of the Command Trust Network, the implant registry and information clearinghouse we'd consulted two years ago, she found a surgeon who was expert in the removal of "Même" and "Replicon" implants. This surgery excised a greater amount of tissue than she expected, leaving her more disfigured than she would have been with a simple mastectomy. As a single woman, she finds the sense of mutilation particularly painful. She, too, has begun to pursue legal action.

Last spring, Ronnie's doctor finally decided to biopsy the nodule he'd been following in the breast where he'd performed a lumpectomy four years before. To his surprise, it was another breast cancer, probably another primary cancer. This time, he recommended a mastectomy. Despite potential problems of reconstruction following radiation treatment, which can make the skin less elastic and more difficult to work with, Ronnie chose to have immediate reconstruction with a tissue expander, as I did.

Her results, once she was inflated and a saline-filled implant was inserted, were disappointing. The implant was half-grapefruit shaped, rather than having a natural tear-drop form, and it was much too high on her chest wall. Recently, another surgery, performed by a different surgeon, gave her a better result by changing the position of the "pocket" and partially releasing one of her pectoral muscles.

One year ago, following a full course of treatment with the new drug Taxol, Pat completed her autologous bone marrow transplant (ABMT)—a misnomer, actually, for it was stem cells from her blood, not her bone marrow (which can itself be contaminated with cancer cells and is not as effective in rapidly restoring the immune system) that were reinfused (transplanted), following massive doses of chemotherapy that would otherwise have destroyed her resistance to disease.

Still healthy despite all her previous treatment, Pat weathered the transplant better than anyone expected, spending only a couple of weeks in the hospital and remaining free of the serious and potentially fatal infections that ABMT sometimes produces. Her response was not unusual, however. This new method, now referred to as "high-dose chemotherapy (HDC) with stem cell harvest and reinfusion," has proved to be much safer. Because the immune system recovers faster, the use of stem cells has cut down significantly on the rate of serious infections, which had previously led to a mortality rate as high as five percent from the ABMT procedure itself.

Recovering her stamina took longer, but this winter, Pat and her husband were able to take a strenuous and rewarding trip to Mexico and Guatemala. Life began to seem normal again. Pat was finally back at work, feeling energetic despite residual joint pain, when the next bad news hit. One of her tumor-markers, a measure of undetected cancer cell growth in the body, was elevated. Scans revealed a spot on her sternum, and possibly one in her lungs. Two years after her first recurrence, the cancer was back. The most aggressive treatment she could find had bought her less than a year's respite.

The news of Pat's latest recurrence was a shock to me and somehow unanticipated, despite what my rational mind told me about her prognosis. The vehement optimism she had displayed throughout her treatment had all but convinced me she would be okay, at least for a long while. Her fighting attitude was, and is, impressive—as impressive, in its way, as Miriam's calm sense of resignation and acceptance.

"I don't want to think about dying," Pat told the group last year before her transplant. "I'm going for a cure. I'm planning on being one of that ten percent that survives five years."

Two depressing days passed between the time I heard the latest bad news from Pat's husband and my first conversation with her about it. After we finally spoke on the telephone, and she filled me in on the next set of treatment possibilities—some experimental, some using different combinations of drugs—in such a matter-of-fact way, I felt much better. There were still new strategies to be tried; there was still hope.

Strange as it might seem, there was a certain relief in hearing the bad news, Pat told the group when we met. "The worst is the waiting, not knowing where and when it will turn up next." Now she could do something besides wait by the telephone for test results from her oncologist. She could marshal her resources, decide on the next course of chemotherapy and work on getting her health insurance to cover the costs of her treatment.

Pat didn't want to discuss with us her prognosis or her fears of dying. "I want to focus on living," she said. "Nothing else makes any sense."

To get through aggressive treatment was struggle enough, as Pat already knew; now she discovered she would have to fight for the treatment itself. Claiming it was not "medically necessary," Metropolitan Life denied Pat's predetermination request for a second high dose chemotherapy (HDC) with stem-cell harvest and reinfusion, using different and more effective anti-cancer drugs. A second attempt was not "reasonable," the insurance company said, since she had "failed" her prior HDC in less than a year. (Accepted medical terminology persists in this bizarre reversal of terms. The truth is, of course, that the treatment failed her, not the other way around.)

Pat's lawyers filed for a preliminary injunction so her treatment could proceed. A federal judge heard expert testimony from her oncologist, as well as from the doctor who made the insurance determination.

Appropriate only for young, strong women with a small amount of measurable tumor, a repeat HDC with stem-cell or bone-marrow reinfusion has only been attempted in a few cases of metastatic breast cancer thus far, although it has become an accepted treatment in advanced leukemia and Hodgkin's disease. When Pat went to court, Duke University had enrolled twenty-seven women with metastatic breast cancer in a protocol testing both double and repeat HDC with stem-cell reinfusion. Dana Farber Cancer Center in Boston has reported success with double transplants, where two HDCs with stem-cell reinfusion are done a month apart.

Pat's oncologist testified that, in his estimation, the repeat procedure should give her a 15 to 20% chance at long term survival or cure. Without it, he stated flatly, she would die in a matter of months.

It was obvious to all of us in the courtroom that the insurance company was concerned with the precedent this case might set. While HDC with bone-marrow or stem-cell reinfusion is now a widely performed treatment for metastatic breast cancer, scores of women all over the country have been refused coverage for this procedure. This judge alone had heard three such cases in the past six months, he told the attorney for Met Life, pointing out that her policy specifically covered chemotherapy—all chemotherapy. "There is every indication that it will extend her life to some extent," the judge said. "I think the odds are reasonable."

Before the judge could grant the preliminary injunction, Met Life offered a settlement, agreeing to pay 100% of Pat's medical expenses, as well as her legal fees. It was a victory, and an enormous relief. Still outraged at this legal ordeal, Pat and her husband could at least take some comfort in knowing that her case will help other women.

But it's easy to become fixated on the dramatic and distressing struggles and ignore the quiet victories. Lest it seem that most of our remaining group of eight women is continually beset with cancer-related problems, I should emphasize that Penny, Anne, Rosa, Helen and I have had no active disease or treatment for at least two years. But when our group meets, we always have plenty to talk about. We are friends, now, beyond our shared bond.

This book is difficult for me to end, for the ending is still open, the future unknown. But that's a fact of life with which we all contend, whether or not a life-threatening illness has entered our lives. Although I have not recaptured my former self, physically or emotionally, I do feel recovered.

Paradoxically, the largest part of this sense of recovery is the acknowledgement that for me breast cancer is not yet "over," if in fact it ever will be. There are continual losses, triumphs, changes—in my life, and in those of the other women I've learned to love and admire.

A women who befriends other women with breast cancer will, over time, outlive some of her friends, or they will outlive her. It is a risk we all take knowingly. With Miriam's death, this has begun to happen to me.

Coming to know other women with breast cancer, especially those in my support group, has transformed the anxiety-ridden experience of living with the disease from a solitary ordeal to a rich and shared encounter.

Titling this memoir, I found myself hesitant to use the word "survivor." Many women with breast cancer claim this descriptor as a sign of their courage and endurance, of the joy of being alive *now*, as well as a symbol of hope for a disease-free future.

My dictionary defines a survivor as one who exists longer than another, one who outlives. Apart from its overuse in self-help jargon, my reluctance to term myself a "survivor" is half a superstition over tempting fate, half a perhaps-misplaced sense of disloyalty to Miriam and the near-ly two hundred thousand other breast cancer "victims" who have died in the four years since my diagnosis.

Most but not all of the women I know with metastatic disease have had lymph-node involvement, indicating their disease had already spread at the time it was first discovered. Because their cancers are presumably more advanced at diagnosis or more rapidly growing, such women often have their recurrences sooner, and are also more likely, overall, to ex-perience a recurrence.

But none of us feels really safe. As Dr. Susan Love points out, "20 to 30 percent of women with negative nodes will still get metastatic breast cancer and sooner or later die of it." By the most optimistic estimates, survival statistics for breast cancer are still grim, with overall longterm mortality at about a third.

And the disease does not always recur where we expect it to. Recently, I met a woman who considered herself cured. With only microscopic calcifications on her mammogram at diagnosis, and aggressive treatment at her insistence, with mastectomy and chemotherapy, she had been deemed at lowest risk, with more than a ninety percent chance of cure. Six years post-diagnosis, her biggest worry was that the three small bumps that suddenly appeared beneath the skin on her chest wall might be silicone from a ruptured implant. On biopsy, they turned out to be recurrences of her original cancer.

Stories like this eat away at our optimism, undermining the quiet dis-tinctions we make between ourselves and the women we know who are coping with metastatic disease. We'll be okay, we tell ourselves. We didn't have lymph-node involvement. Or our tumors were small, or had differentiated margins, or were ER-positive, or our chemo treatments were unusually aggressive. Or we just "know" we are cured, somehow. There's no cancer in our bodies.

The reassurance that women with breast cancer seek remains just out of reach, obscured by a confusing welter of factors we are ill-equipped to evaluate. We read and reread the statistics, knowing they describe the aggregate, that drawing any conclusions about our own individual chances is senseless.

The word cure has less meaning than we would like it to have, with a disease that can recur unpredictably at any time, after many years. Ten-year disease-free survival, according to Dr. Ezra Greenspan, president of the Chemotherapy Foundation, can be considered "the clinical equivalent of cure." But is it, really? We all know of women who have died in the twelfth or eighteenth or twentieth year after diagnosis.

Despite little change in the overall death rate from breast cancer over the past several decades, there are hopeful signs regarding breast cancer treatment, according to Chemotherapy Foundation figures. After ten years of "optimal" therapy, the more aggressive adjuvant chemohormonal treatments (combination chemotherapy and/or tamoxifen immediately after surgery) are finally beginning to demonstrate real increases in survival rates.

Before 1988, when several studies confirmed the efficacy of aggressive adjuvant chemotherapy for treatment of early breast cancers, combination chemohormonal therapy was usually offered in "non-optimal underdosage" to Stage II patients, considered higher risk, and not at all to Stage I patients, considered lower risk. The depressing survival figures in my breast cancer text reflect this trend.

To insure that those women who really need these potent drugs will receive them, new methods of discriminating risk for recurrence are now in use, and others are being perfected all the time, using sophisticated analyses of cell pathology and genetic materials.

Dr. Greenspan makes the claim that fifteen thousand women—nearly a third of those who will die this year from breast cancer—could be saved each year with optimal adjuvant chemohormonal treatment. If these more aggressive multi-drug treatments are as effective as Dr. Greenspan and others say, mortality rates from breast cancer, which have remained fundamentally unchanged for half a century, should decrease dramatically as the decade wears on.

Recent findings have associated optimal chemotherapy treatment with the big cancer research centers in urban areas, while physicians elsewhere often continue to undertreat. "Until recently," Dr. Greenspan explains, "both the lay public and many physicians and surgeons actually believed that chemotherapy was essentially palliative (temporarily controlling) but could not really be curative in breast cancer." This skeptical attitude certainly prevailed in the textbook on breast cancer that I read when I was first diagnosed.

Residual medical bias against prompt, optimal-dosage chemotherapy, especially in older patients, is certain to change over the next decade, if the data is there to support it. "After looking back at 133 controlled trials involving 77,000 patients over a 10-15 year period," Dr. Greenspan writes, "even the most emphatic nay-sayers admit that various chemotherapy combinations improve the chances of disease free survival significantly with a risk reduction of up to 30-45 percent."

Attitudes in the population at large are bound to follow, as chemotherapy is redefined in the public mind as life-giving, rather than a treatment of last resort reserved for the terminally ill.

Approved by the FDA in late 1992 for use in ovarian cancer, the new drug Taxol and its synthetic cousin, Taxotere, have shown great promise in treating metastatic breast cancer so far in clinical trials.

The anti-estrogen tamoxifen (brand name, Nolvadex, which I've been taking, with minimal side effects, for two and a half years now) has shown particular efficacy in reducing by half the incidence of contralateral (in the other breast) cancer, even for ER-negative patients. A large controlled study has gotten underway this past year to determine if tamoxifen can prevent or delay breast cancer in women at high risk.

New experimental treatments that work in different ways, by boosting immune system functioning, are also under investigation. Known as "biological response modifiers," these include lymphokines like interkeukin-2, tumor necrosis factor, and interferon. Colony stimulating factor, or CSF, similar to the substance given to Pat and Miriam while they were on Taxol, allows administration of higher doses of chemotherapy by stimulating the bone marrow.

Of course, these hopeful developments don't eradicate the uncertainty women feel now. Because breast cancer can recur after ten or even twenty years, the much-touted five-year survival mark means less than it does with some other cancers. Dr. Susan Love advises women with breast cancer to think of it like asthma or diabetes—as a chronic disease, something that you live with for a long time.

Meanwhile, the research continues and expands. Next month or next year, a new treatment may be discovered to prolong survival, perhaps indefinitely. Extended periods of remission, during which life can be lived with relative normality, can become a worthy goal in themselves.

A long time is not the same as a lifetime, but it's a lot to a woman with metastatic disease. Six years after her 1978 mastectomy, poet Audre Lorde was told her cancer had spread to her liver. She lived for almost ten more years, a victory by any definition.

We stand on the edge of a new era of early prevention, diagnosis and treatment of breast cancer. Women are mobilized now, and won't rest until this leading killer of women is eradicated or at least controlled. Dr. Love believes this will happen in her lifetime: "It's nice to think that, in my old age, my expertise won't be that of a practitioner but of an historian, recounting, to a disbelieving audience, what it was like back in the days when breast cancer killed people."

Onto the featureless canvas of what is to come, each cancer patient inevitably paints her own blend of fears and aspirations. On bad days, when nagging doubts creep in, she imagines never seeing her children or grandchildren grown, and leaving her husband alone, bereft. On good days, when the experience seems like nothing more than a bad dream, fading into the remote past, the promise of the future does not taunt but tantalize, and she dares to make plans again.

Most days, I can visualize a future. I find myself talking heedlessly of distant plans with something approaching the confidence of pre-diagnosis times—and without the sickening drop I used to feel, that nasty, gut-wrenching shock that nagged: "But what if you're not around?"

Finally, I am doing what others had advised me to do all along: getting on with my life, and letting the specter of cancer recede into the past. This is not something I could have managed much before now.

I remember how bitterly I resented those who blithely suggested that I get on with my usual activities. They were right, of course. Like so many important realizations, this one cannot come from others, but has to be fashioned from the whole cloth of long personal experience. It is a matter of timing, of waiting until the release of all these complicated emotions and attachments no longer seems a betrayal of self.

More and more, I am finding—at least between checkups—that my passport locates me back in the kingdom of the well, as Susan Sontag so aptly put it. There is some sort of quiet rebuilding going on, as if the infrastructure of my spirit is being shored up.

It is four years and more now from the date of my mastectomy. For some in our support group, it is more than six years since diagnosis. We celebrate each other's anniversaries.

This past January, Tom arranged a fiftieth birthday party for me with family and friends. All of the women in my breast cancer support group were there. We toasted ourselves, and one another.

The next day, we gathered for Miriam's memorial service in upstate New York, where we discovered that the softly falling snow and windless night had conspired to create a fairy tale Currier and Ives winter landscape, with each bare branch and hemlock limb trimmed in feathery white.

Despite Gary's reassurances, I'd been concerned about the conjunction of my birthday celebration and Miriam's memorial on the same weekend. It might seem wrong, inappropriate: a night spent dancing before a day spent mourning.

I needn't have worried. One by one we stood before the big fieldstone fireplace of the home Miriam and Gary had built together, and spoke of her, and of ourselves and each other. As the afternoon passed, and the light shaded into violet, the beauty outside was matched by the warmth within. Grateful for the moment, we sat with our husbands and friends, smiling through tears.

I recognized the bittersweet feeling like an old friend, and found it strangely comforting. There was a sort of grace to this helplessness, I thought to myself, an open-handed, open-hearted acceptance of what is, flowing effortlessly through and around all the events of my life like that muddy river in faraway Nepal.

There was nothing beyond that room, nothing more we needed from ourselves or each other that day, as we sat there together, allowing grief to mingle seamlessly with celebration. Without effort, without anguish, fear receded, and the future ceased its tyranny.

It was the closest thing to healing I had found in all these years of crisis. Perhaps it is the closest any of us will ever come.

I am holding in my hand a small roundish stone, perhaps an inch and a half in diameter and irregularly shaped, of a nondescript dark gray flecked with white. Its only claim to distinction are the dozen tiny barnacles that cling to its surface, although of course it is only their outer shells, their skeletons, so to speak, that remain.

There are many other stones — not to mention shells — scattered around my apartment, on bookshelves and mantelpiece, culled from many walks on beaches over the years: bits of glazed ceramic tile from the Algarve, smooth black lozenges with threads of white quartz from Ischia, tide-smoothed blossoms of coral from the coast of the Yucatan.

Each object contains within it the memory of some particular place. I can hold one in my hand and conjure up a specific day, see again the whitecaps on the water, clouds scudding across a threatening sky, shorebirds stalking the curve of a rocky shore. Another will call to mind a perfectly empty beach early in the morning when the Aegean is as still as a pond, with two young men carefully setting out row after row of brightly striped umbrellas and canvas chairs on the black sand.

This particular stone I didn't discover for myself. It arrived in a surprisingly large box one day, postmarked North Truro, Massachusetts, with a note from a friend. She had been thinking of me as she walked along the beach that day, and hoped I was feeling better.

I hold the stone in my hand, turning it this way and that. Ah, well. Someone else's souvenir is never as evocative as one's own, I think to myself, fighting the thinnest edge of disappointment at this secondhand gift from the sea.

Since the stone contains no memory of place for me, I am free to invent the moment of its discovery. And so I imagine it tangled up in one of those complex clusters of flotsam and jetsam you find on ocean beaches. A many-branched skein of dark, ribbonlike seaweed, the kind that invites you to pop its bubble-like flotation chambers but defeats your efforts with its leathery skin, has bound together fragments of driftwood, mussel shells, black skates' egg cases, with the inevitable bits of human refuse — a length of frayed rope, some knotted fishing line, an orange cork float — in an assemblage so artfully arranged by the waves that it would not look out of place on a pedestal in an art museum.

I can almost see my friend strolling on the deserted beach at Truro, high cliffs of sand at her back, a stiff wind blowing the long tight curls of her graying hair this way and that. I see her bend to disentangle my stone from the rest of the cluster, brush off the sand and pocket it. Her loose-fitting sundress, the brown bare feet and strong mannish hands with paint under the close cropped nails—all of these are perfectly clear in my mind's eye.

She takes the stone again from her pocket and examines it closely. The barnacles are like little white teeth, each an open dome with its tiny door closed. There's something touching about the delicacy and tenacity of these small creatures, something about the way they hold on, refusing to be worn down by the waves or swept away by the currents, that makes her feel better about her own life.

Later that day, she wraps up the stone to send it to me. She hesitates, and wonders if perhaps she should keep it for herself.

Then she decides to send it after all.

Reaching Out

The National Alliance of Breast Cancer Organizations (NABCO)
(212) 719-0154, Monday–Friday 9 a.m.–5 p.m. EST. Or write NAB-
CO at 1180 Avenue of the Americas, Second Floor New York, New
York 10036.

> Provides free fact sheets and *NABCO News* articles on treatment
> options and an annually updated "Breast Cancer Resource List," a
> comprehensive listing of regional support organizations and many
> other resources for gathering information and help. An excellent
> place to begin.

American Cancer Society Cancer Response System
(800) ACS-2345, Monday–Friday 8:30 a.m.–5 p.m. EST.

> Sponsors Reach to Recovery, provides information on early detec-
> tion and treatment, and refers callers to cancer centers and support
> groups.

Cancer Information Service (National Cancer Institute)
(800) 4CANCER, Monday–Friday 9 a.m.–10 p.m. EST. In Alaska:
(800) 638-6070. In Oahu, Hawaii: 524-1234. Call collect from neighbor islands.

> Provides referrals to cancer centers, specialists and support groups.
> Offers information on treatment options, including ongoing clini-
> cal trials.

Susan G. Komen Breast Cancer Information Help Line
(800) IM-AWARE, Monday–Friday 9 a.m.–6 p.m. EST.

> The Komen Alliance provides written and spoken information on
> risk analysis, early detection, diagnosis, treatment and referrals.

Y-Me, National Organization for Breast Cancer Information and Support
(800) 221-2141, Monday–Friday 10 a.m.–6 p.m. EST or (708) 799-8228 24 hours.
> Phones are answered by breast cancer survivors, who provide emotional support (not medical advice) and refer callers to local cancer centers.

The YWCA Encore Program
> Offers rehabilitative exercise and supportive discussions for breast cancer patients. Check with your local Y for the program nearest you.

The National Breast Cancer Coalition
P.O. Box 66373, Washington, D.C. 20035
> Active in advocacy work, influencing private and public health policy. They need our support.

NOTE: These are national resources. Locally, your community probably has an ongoing support/advocacy group which can help you (check NABCO list, above). Major hospitals may have support groups through their Breast Centers, Departments of Social Work, or Psychiatry.

Acknowledgments

My deepest gratitude is to the dozens of women, too many to name here, whose stories have touched and inspired me over the last several years. Although they, too, will go nameless here, I hope that my support group leader, oncologist, breast surgeon and plastic surgeon—and their staffs—know how grateful I am for their skill and compassion.

Thanks are due to my agent, Gloria Loomis, for persevering; to my editor, Fiona McCrae, for her delicacy and intelligence in working on my manuscript; and to Bill Corbett, for leading me to Faber and Faber in the first place.

I can't possibly express adequate thanks to my friends and family, especially to my brother-in-law Donald Mayer, for his strength and devotion. As to my husband Tom's good humor, stalwart support and tenderness—what more could any woman hope for?